A Continental Shelf

90 0573312 9

BOSCH Supported by Robert Bosch Limited

bsis Matched

A Continental Shelf

Books across Europe from Ptolemy to Don Quixote

An exhibition to mark the re-opening of the
Bodleian Exhibition Room

Bodleian Library
Oxford
1994

ISBN 1-85124-037-3

Published with the assistance of Robert Bosch Limited, an award winner under the Business Sponsorship Incentive Scheme for its support of the Bodleian Library. The BSIS is a Government Scheme administered by ABSA (Association for Business Sponsorship of the Arts).

Design from
The Drawing Room, Warwick

Printed by
Sherwood Press
Nottingham Limited

Contents

Preface

In his short autobiography Sir Thomas Bodley wrote that to achieve success his library needed to be furnished with four essentials. They were: the time and the funding to enable the work to go forward, the scholarship necessary to maintain it, and a succession of 'honourable friends' to support it. The wisdom of his words is apparent throughout this exhibition. Sir Thomas's library opened in 1602 and the time since then has allowed great collections to be made. If there have been periods during these four centuries when the Bodleian Library has had few funds of its own, it is then that its benefactors have shown true friendship in helping it to build these collections. There has, by contrast, rarely been a shortage of scholarship in its staff, and it is exemplified once again in this exhibition which is the work of Dr Kristian Jensen of the Special Collections Division of the Department of Printed Books and Dr Martin Kauffmann of the Department of Western Manuscripts. Drawing on the additional expertise of their colleagues they have selected, annotated and displayed some fifty-seven items - highlights from collections built up largely from the generosity of benefactors - and show them in a setting which is the latest example of such generosity.

The names of those who have enabled the Bodleian Library to redesign its Exhibition Room are recorded in the room itself. Here we wish to acknowledge with particular gratitude the sponsorship of the Bosch Group for this opening exhibition, illustrating, as it does, the cultural, commercial, artistic, and literary linkages between a variety of communities many of which are now encompassed within the European Union. It is a peculiarly fitting way to celebrate the re-opening of the principal display area in an institution which bears the name of Sir Thomas Bodley - a man whose crowning achievement, after a boyhood spent as a refugee and an adulthood as a diplomat on the European scene, was to found a library in Oxford 'for the republic of the learned'.

David Vaisey
Bodley's Librarian

Foreword

At a time when co-operation between the European nations is advancing through expansion of the European Union and a Single European Market, the Bosch Group is particularly pleased to be associated with this exhibition in which the Bodleian Library demonstrates with examples from its great collections the enormous influence of books in the creation of a European cultural tradition.

The newly-refurbished exhibition room at last enables the library to display its magnificent treasures from all parts of the world in an environment and a manner which they deserve and the Bodleian Library is to be congratulated for both this splendid new addition to its facilities and for the inaugural exhibition.

A Continental Shelf - books across Europe from Ptolemy to Don Quixote also serves to remind visitors that the Library has been, since its re-foundation by Sir Thomas Bodley in 1602, a truly European library and that Bodley himself was a European, having spent some of his childhood in Germany and Switzerland and served as a diplomat in the Netherlands.

The Bosch Group, which has its headquarters in Stuttgart and employs more than 120,000 people in Europe, has benefited from a strong commitment to co-operation between Europeans engaged in its business activities. From the beginning the founder Robert Bosch had a vision of international co-operation and the exchange of new ideas, inspired by experience gained in America, where he worked with Edison, and in London with the Siemens telegraph and electrical company. He founded his "workshop for precision mechanics and electrical engineering" in 1886, and the first Bosch agency outside Germany was established in London in 1898. The associations between Bosch and the United Kingdom are, therefore, extremely close. Throughout his career as industrialist and philanthropist Robert Bosch regarded his company as a means of creating assets for the benefit of society, supporting and encouraging education, medicine and welfare in general, and, above all, international understanding and the unification of Europe.

In keeping with its modern status as an industrial foundation the charitable aims of the Robert Bosch Stiftung GmbH are concerned not only with the promotion of international understanding, but also the support of cultural activities, which is given a high priority by Bosch in all its markets. The Bosch Group does not measure its achievements by commercial success alone: our objectives in the United Kingdom extend much further, beyond our contributions to exports through manufacturing and to employment in a variety of locations. The opening of the Bodleian Library's new exhibition room provides the Foundation with a unique opportunity at once to build upon the international vision of Robert Bosch, and to implement the objectives of the Robert Bosch Stiftung.

Visitors to *A Continental Shelf* - many of whom will be travellers themselves from across Europe - will be privileged to view some of the finest books in the Bodleian Library, displayed in the splendid setting of the new exhibition room. I am delighted to contribute this foreword to a publication which constitutes a permanent and valuable record of books which are themselves monuments of European civilisation.

Dr Marcus Bierich
Chairman of the Supervisory Board
Robert Bosch GmbH

Introduction

Some of the Bodleian's most famous and visually compelling possessions, as well as hidden treasures, have been brought together in this exhibition to give some indication of the scope of the Library's European collections. The manuscripts and printed books exhibited illustrate the cultural unity of Europe in the Middle Ages and Early Modern period. When regarded separately the states of Europe display a surprising degree of internal diversity — social, linguistic, religious and national. When Europe is viewed as a whole, these divisions reveal groups which formed international communities across the borders of states. They were bound together by religion, profession, trade, skill or craft, by nationality, by a real or perceived common inheritance, by shared economic interests, by common languages, or by common literary traditions and genres. Some such communities — religious orders for instance — were bound together by institutions which transcended the borders of states; others were not. The exhibition illustrates the importance of institutionalised communities as well as of those less formally constituted, and even of some which were formally suppressed.

In a politically disunited Europe, one country could provide safe havens for populations persecuted elsewhere. Refugees were frequently the vehicles of contact between parts of Europe, often with long-term effects both for the host country, which could be enriched by the skills and energy of the immigrants, and for the country of origin, to which refugees might return bringing with them new knowledge, new ideas and new attitudes. This cultural cross-fertilisation was made easier because similarities of laws, languages, and religions contributed to the creation of a cultural cohesion, as well as providing focuses for conflicts. Jewish and Muslim communities resident in Europe were especially important groups in this context. As some states do today, royal or other wealthy patrons provided incentives for the skilled and educated to settle in the areas which they controlled. Scholars, scientists and craftsmen actively sought the support of such patrons. Like the political or religious refugees, economically motivated migrants contributed to the creation of European communities, while providing a basis for the further development of skills and knowledge: printers form one such international group of craftsmen, whose high level of mobility ensured that skills and innovations quickly spread throughout Europe. The creation of Europe-wide communities through the mobility of skilled or learned members of the population, is illustrated by many of the items selected for this exhibition.

The exhibition addresses these issues in five separate sections. A small introductory section, 'Shaping the World', sets the scene with maps and guides, showing not only navigational and cartographic developments, but also travel accounts such as pilgrim guides.

'The Classics and Christendom' focusses on models of unity, spiritual and secular, provided by the inheritance from the ancient world. The *Notitia dignitatum*, describing the military bureaucracy of the Roman Empire shortly after its division into East and West in the late 4th century, introduces the Empire as the background for a vision of a politically and religiously united Europe. The fiction of political continuity between ancient and modern empires is nowhere more effectively visualized than in Hubertus Goltzius's portrait medallions of emperors, beginning with Julius Caesar and ending with Philip II of Spain. The Roman Empire reappears in all sections of the exhibition as an ideological myth which provided rulers with an image of European unity. But the structures of spiritual unity were more successful than their purely secular counterparts: the inhabitants of the continent thought of themselves as Christians, not Europeans. Monastic orders were transnational cultural institutions: the Rule of St. Benedict was a work crucial for the organised monastic life of Europe, and many of the books in other sections also exemplify the unifying cultural impact of monastic houses. The Bible, the public liturgy and the shared forms of private devotion were all unifying factors, central to the life of the Church.

In the section 'International Languages — International Learning', we focus on the Latin language, the shared language of religion, learning, and administration which facilitated the mobility of book producers, of the educated classes and of the books they carried with them. Latin was fundamental to the operation of Canon and Roman Law, both of which provided models of centralised authority within Europe. We show first printed editions of Latin and Greek classics produced by Germans and Greeks in Italy for a European market. Latin was also a vital international language for the transmission, not only of philosophy and the arts, but of mathematics, medicine, and natural history, much of it translated into Latin from Greek, often via Arabic. For these purposes it was essential for a common terminology to be used. The creation of a common language of science, and of compatible vernacular languages of science, was essential for the formation of a modern European community of scientists. Hebrew being the third international language of Europe, this section of the exhibition also includes a Hebrew legal commentary, printed in Istanbul by a refugee from Spain.

To balance the picture, the exhibition will trace the development of vernacular languages by the different peoples of Europe. Early written examples often take the form of translations of Latin texts. But gradually we see the emergence of vernacular literature, often in a form which suggests oral recitation: the earliest surviving copy of the *Chanson de Roland*, the earliest masterpiece of French literature, might have fitted into a travelling troubadour's pocket. The fact that the manuscript was produced in England reminds us that even the vernacular languages crossed the boundaries we know today. A shared set of themes and genres made vernacular literature part of the international life of Europe. The vernaculars were not only vehicles of storytelling: translations of Vitruvius's classical texts on architecture helped create a common European architectural idiom, just as there was a common European musical idiom. The impact of translations of scientific, philosophical and religious texts ensured that compatible linguistic expression could be given to a shared store of concepts and notions.

A final section looks at Europe's relations with its neighbours. The identity of Europe was sharpened by the increased knowledge of other worlds, other traditions. We show a Latin translation of an Arabic medical manual which served for centuries as a text book in European schools of medicine. The miniature of Marco Polo leaving Venice forms perhaps the most famous frontispiece to a book of traveller's tales. European expansion was dependent on a greater knowledge of the world. Cortés's navigational manual is one example of the European reliance on technical expertise for its expansion. As we began with maps of Europe, we end with Europeans mastering the globe through their navigational skills, gaining a better understanding of the structure of the universe at large, and mapping the moon.

Most of the books in this exhibition were produced long before the Bodleian Library was founded — in 1602. The holdings of the Bodleian are not primarily based on materials local to the area or even to the country as a whole: its collections are international and have grown over nearly four hundred years, through purchase and donation. The large individual collections presented to the Library, from that of Archbishop Laud in the 1630s to that presented by John Ehrman in 1978, are in themselves documents of the intellectual aspirations of scholars, scientists and collectors. Our selection of books also, therefore, illustrates the history of collecting and the development of an international library, reflecting the wide-ranging interests of Sir Thomas Bodley, of his librarians and of the many benefactors to his foundation. It is hoped that the notes of provenance, briefly listing the history of each volume, will illustrate an enduring Oxford interest in material of great importance for our understanding of our part of the world.

It has been attempted to make the description of manuscripts and printed books as uniform as possible, but some inconsistencies remain. For manuscripts the number of leaves indicates the total number of leaves, including flyleaves and items bound with the work described but not described in the catalogue. For printed books, the number of leaves is the number of leaves of the described item only and does not include flyleaves, but does include blank leaves which form part of the sheets of the book as it left the press. This is in keeping with providing the format of printed books: folio, quarto or octavo [2°, 4°, 8°] indicate whether the book is made up of sheets of paper folded either once, twice or four times after being printed. It has been thought inappropriate, however,to give full information on the collation of the sheets of printed books. Format is not an indication of size: this is given for both manuscripts and printed items, measuring a leaf to the nearest 5 mm. Unless stated otherwise, all manuscripts are on parchment and all printed books on paper. References to literature for printed books often, but not invariably, refer to works on the text or the edition as a whole, whereas most literature for manuscripts refers to work on the individual volume. The standard format of shelfmarks differs slightly for printed books and manuscripts, particularly in the shelfmark 'Auct.'.

The mounting of the exhibition has been very much a cooperative venture, as is indicated in the preface by Bodley's Librarian. With regard specifically to the production of the catalogue, we would like especially to thank the following colleagues for their help and advice: Dr. Bruce Barker-Benfield, Joanna Dodsworth, Clive Hurst, Dana Josephson, Julian Roberts, and Michael Turner. Dr. Judith Field of Birkbeck College, London, provided valuable information on the astronomical and astrological works displayed.

Kristian Jensen
Martin Kauffmann

Abbreviations

BLR *Bodleian Library Record*, 1- (1938-).

Douce Legacy *The Douce Legacy. An Exhibition to Commemorate the 150th Anniversary of the Bequest [to the Bodleian Library] of Francis Douce (1757-1834)* (Oxford, 1984).

P & A O. Pächt and J.J.G. Alexander, *Illuminated Manuscripts in the Bodleian Library*, 3 vols (Oxford, 1966-73).

CLA ii E.A. Lowe, *Codices Latini Antiquiores. A Palaeographical Guide to Latin Manuscripts Prior to the Ninth Century. Part II: Great Britain and Ireland* (2nd edition: Oxford, 1972).

SC F. Madan *et al.*, *Summary Catalogue of Western Manuscripts in the Bodleian Library*, 7 vols (Oxford, 1895-1953).

Survival of Ancient Literature R.W. Hunt *et al.*, *The Survival of Ancient Literature. Catalogue of an Exhibition of Greek and Latin Classical Manuscripts Mainly from Oxford Libraries Displayed on the Occasion of the Triennial Meeting of the Hellenic and Roman Societies 28 July - 2 August 1975* (Oxford, 1975).

'Further Italian Illuminated Manuscripts' A.C. de la Mare, 'Further Italian Illuminated Manuscripts in the Bodleian Library', in *La Miniatura italiana tra gotico e rinascimento I. Atti del II congresso di storia della miniatura italiana, Cortona 24-26 settembre 1981,* ed. E. Sesti (Florence, 1985), 127-54.

Quarto cat. H.O. Coxe *et al.*, *Catalogi Codicum Manuscriptorum Bibliothecae Bodleianae*, 11 vols (Oxford, 1845-1900; revised edition of vol. 2, 1973).

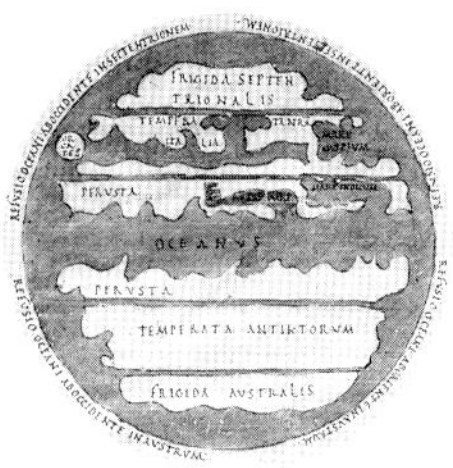

Shaping the World

Maps are graphic representations of human conceptions, not objective purveyors of information. Looking at maps we may begin to understand how people tried to give shape to their world. Maps which to us appear geographically inaccurate may have been made with other purposes in mind than representing the physical shape of the world. For instance, the map in Macrobius's commentary on Cicero's *Somnium Scipionis* (no. 1) is more of a diagram, intended chiefly as an illustration of a cosmological argument in a philosophical work. Other medieval maps were conceived in accordance with the historical geography of human salvation. Maps made for practical use — whether for pilgrims or for traders — often present the world in a form which is closer to the one with which we are familiar, as for instance in the portolan atlas for sailors (no. 2) and the pilgrim guide to the route to Rome (no. 7). The purpose of such maps determines the form which they take, and the features selected vary from map to map. They often did not attempt to depict the entire world, but only those sections which were of direct relevance to their users.

On the other hand, the classical tradition of cartography — derived from Ptolemy — ambitiously attempted to map the entire known world; knowledge of this tradition reached western Europe late (no. 3) and it took some time before the theoretical basis provided by Ptolemy was integrated with information derived from practical mapping traditions. As in so many other areas of knowledge, the classical inheritance had to be fully understood before it could be superseded. Mercator's *Atlas* (no. 4) shows how the classical inheritance was integrated with modern theories of mapping and how theoretical and practical approaches, never entirely separate, were now working together: information from traders and explorers was comprehensively employed in Mercator's ambitious project to create a modern replacement for Ptolemy. These maps could have a political function, providing details about the area controlled or coveted by a ruler and, by extension, they could serve as illustrations of the grandeur of royal or imperial powers. The European interest in mapping the world was part of the drive towards controlling the world.

Shaping the World

Conceptions of the World

1 Macrobius, Commentary on the *Somnium Scipionis* (with Cicero, *Orationes Caesarianae, De Amicitia, De Senectute;* Pseudo-Jerome, *Ad Dardanum de diversis generibus musicorum*).
Southern Germany; late 10th or early 11th century.
i + 115 leaves; 240 x 170 mm.

The most common pattern for maps of the world in medieval Europe was to show the three known continents, Asia (at the top), Europe, and Africa, with the Mediterranean, the River Don, and the Nile forming a T-shaped division between them. Some Roman and Biblical place-names are often included on such maps, with Jerusalem at the centre to emphasize its place in the history of human salvation.

The map exhibited is of a different and rarer kind. The world is divided into five zones: the equatorial region is divided by an ocean, with temperate and polar zones to north and south. Geographical detail is scarce. The land masses are surrounded by the ocean: the legends round the circumference give the direction of the peripheral currents. This conception of the world, a development of the Greek theory of temperature zones developed by Crates of Mallos at Pergamum about 150 BC, was transmitted to the Latin West by two pagan authors of the 4th-5th century AD, whose works became standard medieval textbooks - Macrobius and Martianus Capella. The description of the earth in Macrobius's Commentary on Cicero's *Somnium Scipionis* was usually accompanied by a map.

It is a commonplace that medieval Europeans believed their world to be flat; but several of the most commonly available texts on the subject described it as spherical. Many medieval writers accepted this, though some thought it unlikely that the other side of the world was inhabited. Medieval rulers held an orb, not a disk, to symbolize their power.

Provenance: Isaac Verburg sale, Amsterdam, 1746, lot 486 (at that time still part of the same manuscript as MS. D'Orville 95); J.P. D'Orville (1696-1751); bought by the Bodleian with the rest of the D'Orville collection in 1804.

Literature: SC 16955; P & A i, no. 28; *Survival of Ancient Literature* no. 107; B.C. Barker-Benfield, 'A Ninth-century Manuscript from Fleury: *Cato de Senectute cuMacrobio*', in *Medieval Learning and Literature. Essays Presented to Richard William Hunt*, eds. J.J.G. Alexander, M.T. Gibson (Oxford, 1976), 145-65, pp. 160-64; B. Munk Olsen, *L'Etude des auteurs classiques latins aux XIe et XIIe siècles*, I (Paris, 1982), 246-7, II (Paris, 1985), 338; A.-D. von den Brincken, *Fines Terrae. Die Enden der Erde und der vierte Kontinent auf mittelalterlichen Weltkarten* (Hanover, 1992), XVI, 39, and Abb.6.

MS. D'Orville 77 (fol. 100r)

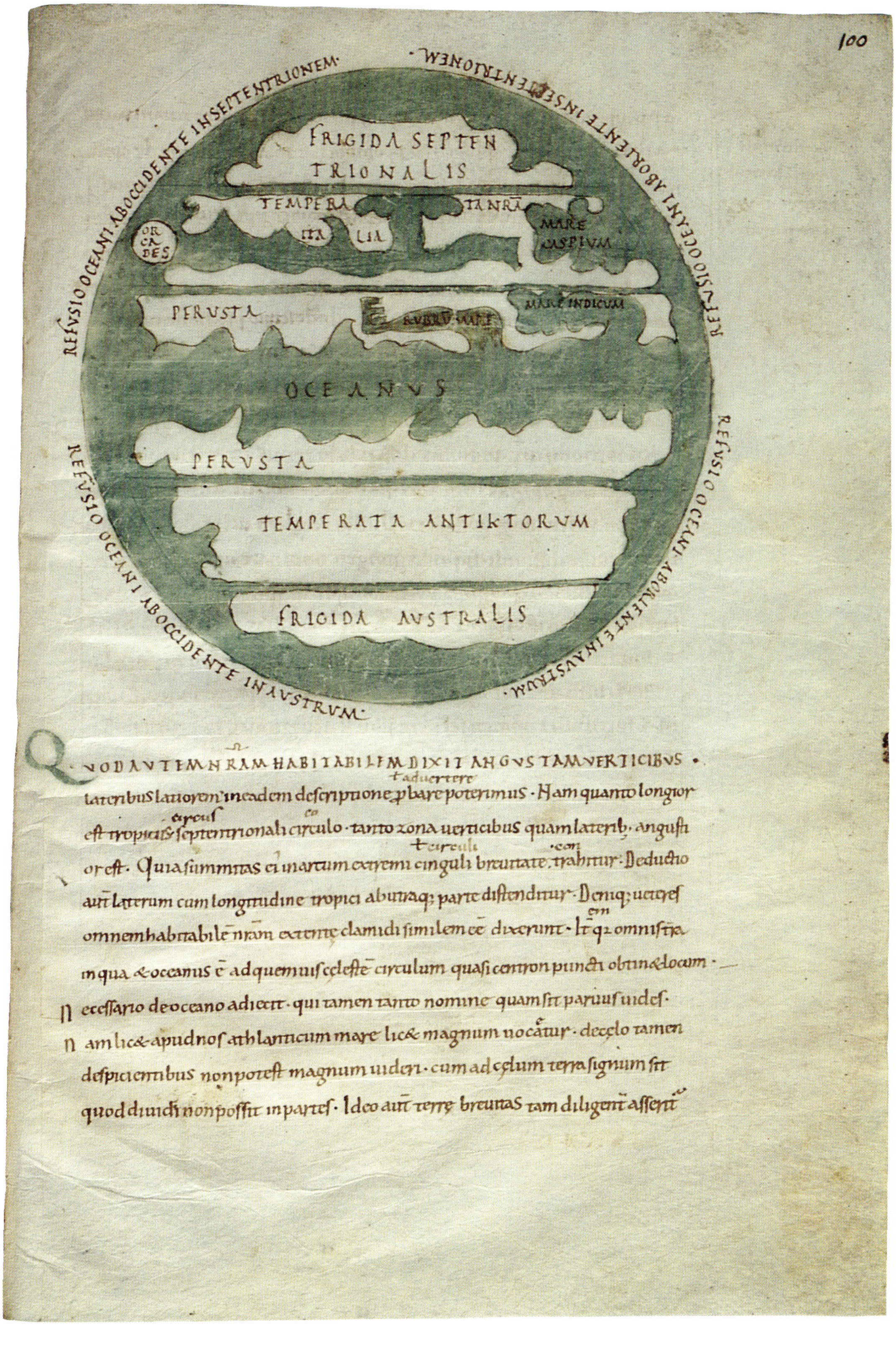
100
REFVSIO OCEANI AB OCCIDENTE IN SEPTENTRIONEM ·
REFVSIO OCEANI AB ORIENTE IN SEPTENTRIONEM ·
FRIGIDA SEPTEN
TRIONALIS
TEMPERA
TANRA
ITA LIA
OR CA DES
MARE CASPIUM
PERUSTA
RUBRU MARE
MARE INDICUM
OCEANUS
PERUSTA
TEMPERATA ANTIKTORUM
FRIGIDA AUSTRALIS
REFVSIO OCEANI AB OCCIDENTE IN AVSTRVM ·
REFVSIO OCEANI AB ORIENTE IN AVSTRVM ·
QVOD AVTEM NRAM HABITABILEM DIXIT ANGVSTAM VERTICIBVS ·
t aduertere
lateribus latiorem in eadem descriptione probare poterimus · Nam quanto longior
circus co
est tropicus septentrionali circulo · tanto zona uerticibus quam lateribus angusti
t circuli con
or est · Quia summitas ei in artum extremi cinguli breuitate trahitur · Deductio
aut laterum cum longitudine tropici ab utraq; parte distenditur · Denique ueteres
gm
omnem habitabilem nram extente clamidi similem ee dixerunt · Itq; omnis terra
in qua & oceanus e ad quemuis celestem circulum quasi centron puncti obtinet locum ·
Necessario de oceano adiecit · qui tamen tanto nomine quam sit paruus uides ·
Nam lic& apud nos athlanticum mare lic& magnum uocatur · de celo tamen
despicientibus non potest magnum uideri · cum ad celum terra signum sit
quod diuidi non possit in partes · Ideo aut terre breuitas tam diligent asseritur

Navigation

2 Portolan atlas.
Venice; *c.*1400.
10 leaves; 290 x 140 mm.

The cartographic content of medieval maps of the world was usually determined by theological considerations; it is portolan charts and atlases which are the most geographically realistic maps of medieval Europe. Normally they cover the Mediterranean and the Black Sea, the area of greatest interest to Venetian and Genoese traders, sometimes extending along the Atlantic coast from Morocco to the British Isles. To sailors on the Mediterranean, distances and direction were vital: portolans are the first cartographic documents regularly to display a linear scale, and are covered by networks of interconnecting rhumb lines. The earliest extant examples date from the late 13th century, and already present a highly accurate outline of the Mediterranean,and a wealth of place-names. Their origins and initial processes of construction remain largely a mystery; but the consistency of their conventions indicates that portolans belong in some sense to a single family. There is no top or bottom: the charts were intended to be rotated. With the three basic navigational aids - chart, lodestone (a magnetized needle), and sandglass - sailors were able to estimate their position. Astronomical navigation made little impact in this world: early astrolabes were too inexact to be used for such relatively small distances.

The physical form of this example is that of an atlas designed for use on board ship. It consists of seven separate charts on parchment, pasted onto the 'pages' of a wooden codex to obviate distortion or shrinkage: if joined, they would form a continuous chart from the Black Sea to the Bristol Channel. The charts are protected by thick outer wooden boards, and a carrying case of wood covered with leather. Despite these features, this is clearly a de-luxe copy, probably never put to practical use. The wood of the covers is inlaid with ivory and coloured woods; the leather of the case is elaborately incised with floral decoration; the first and last openings contain painted devotional diptychs (the Annunciation at the beginning, St. Mark (the patron saint of Venice) and St. Paul (a traveller on the Mediterranean) at the end; and it is in perfect condition.

Provenance: bequeathed to the Bodleian by Francis Douce (1757-1834).

Literature: SC 21965; P & A ii, no. 448; *Douce Legacy* no. 64; Tony Campbell, 'Portolan Charts from the Late Thirteenth Century to 1500', in *The History of Cartography. I: Cartography in Prehistoric, Ancient, and Medieval Europe and the Mediterranean*, eds. J.B. Harley, D. Woodward (Chicago, 1987), 371-463.

MS. Douce 390 (fols. 4v-5r)

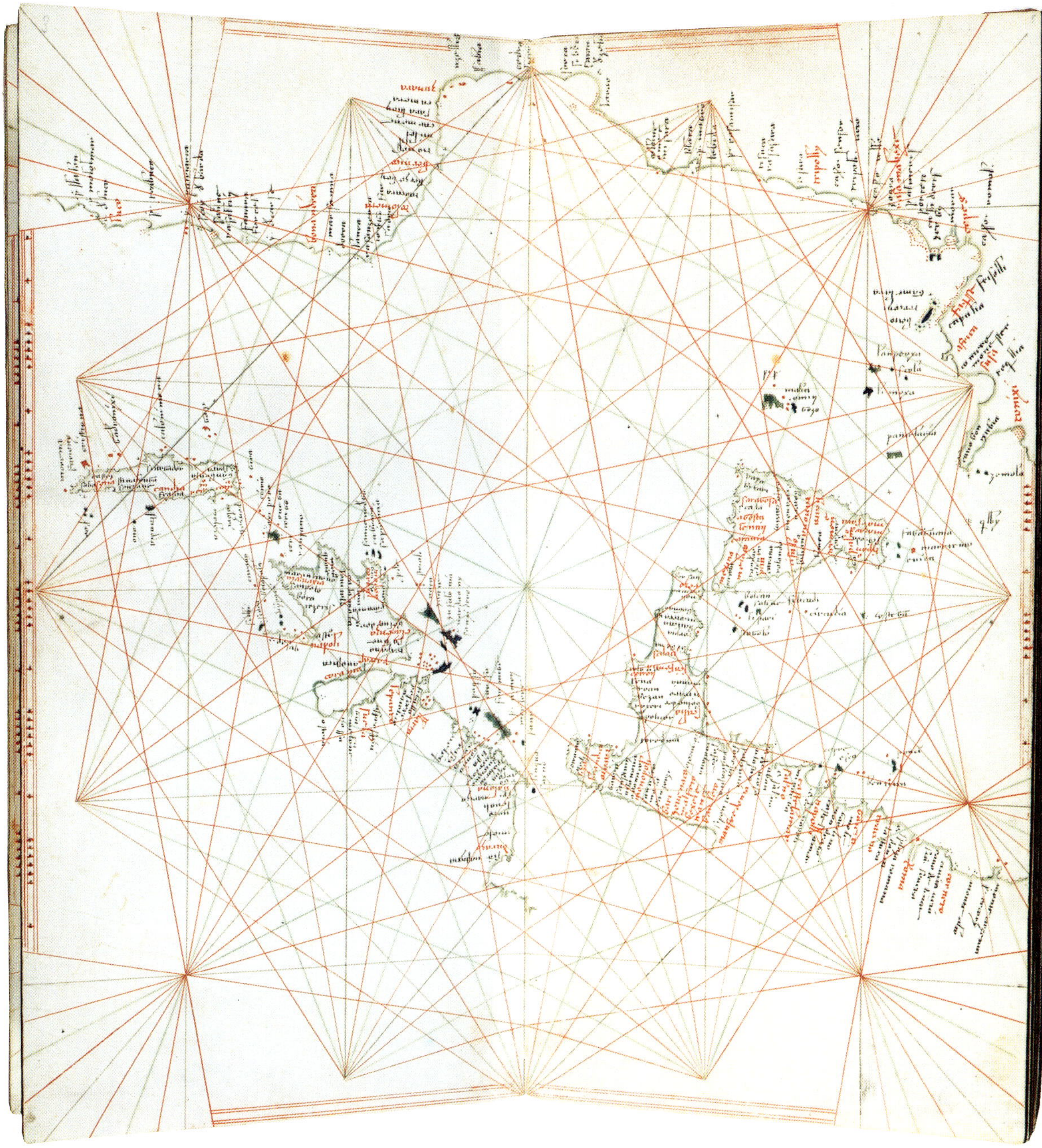

The Beginning of Cartography

3 Ptolemy, *Cosmographia*.
Ulm: Johannes Reger, 1486, 2°, with the maps from the edition Ulm: Lienhart Holl, 1482, 2°. 194 leaves; 420 x 290 mm.

Ptolemy composed his *Cosmographia* in Alexandria in Egypt, *c.*160 AD. He provided coordinates for some 8000 places, tied into a grid of longitudes and latitudes — his major contribution to cartography. The earliest datable maps found with the text are by Maximos Planudes (*c.*1260-1310). He aimed to follow Ptolemy's instructions and his maps must be close to those Ptolemy himself might have compiled. The map of the world, shown here, is drawn up by a certain Agathodaimon from Alexandria whose dates are unknown. In this edition, the map also gives the name of the man who cut the block from which it was printed, a 'Johannes woodcutter from Armsheim'.

In Antiquity the important political and cultural unity was the Empire, on all three continents round the Mediterranean. This constitutes the world of the African Ptolemy. The transmission of Ptolemy in western Europe began with a translation into Latin by Jacopo d'Angelo shortly before 1409, an early example of Italian humanist translations from the Greek. At about the same time, the maps were redrawn with Latin inscriptions; they were later revised by Nicolaus Germanus. The Ulm editions are based on his third recension of the maps dating from *c.*1468. While the other maps which go with Ptolemy were constructed from the text, Nicolaus Germanus added modern maps of Italy, Spain, France and Palestine, and extended the world map to include more of Africa and Scandinavia. This volume is therefore not only an expression of the recovery of classical knowledge, but also of the beginning of a slow process of integrating modern insights with the classical inheritance. The political significance of maps was just as strong in the 15th century as when they were first made. Printed in Germany, and containing the first printed modern map of Spain, our volume belonged to King Ferdinand and Queen Isabella of Spain, whose coat of arms is in the book.

Provenance: Ferdinand and Isabella of Spain: presented in Burgos, 25 August 1492, to Francesco Capello, Venetian ambassador to Spain; bequeathed to the Bodleian by Francis Douce (1757-1834).

Literature: P. Amelung, *Der Frühdruck im deutschen Südwesten 1473-1500. Eine Ausstellung der Württembergischen Landesbibliothek. I. Ulm* (Stuttgart, 1979), 279-87, 329-31; Tony Campbell, *The Earliest Printed Maps 1472-1500* (London, 1987), on Ptolemy pp. 122- 138 (with bibliography).

Douce 305 (fols. 131v-132r: map 1).

CAVRVS·CHORVS·VEL·IAPIX·SIVE·ARGESTES
AQVILO·VEL·BOREAS
CECIAS·APELIOTES
FAVONIVS·ZEPHIRVS
SVBSOLANVS
EVROPA
ASIA
LIBIA·INTERIOR
AFRICA
ETHIOPIA·INTERIOR
MARE·INDICVM
MARE·INDICVM
MARE
PRASODVM
AFRICVS·VEL·LIBS
LIBONOTVS·EVROAVSTER
EVRNOTVS
VVLTVRNVS·EVRVS

Cartography meets Navigation

4 Gerardus Mercator, *Atlas, sive Cosmographicae meditationes de fabrica mundi et fabricati figura.*
Düsseldorf: A. Busius, 1595, 2°; 57 leaves + 108 maps; the sheets with text belonging to type A, the sheets with maps belonging to type B; 425 x 280 mm.

The *Atlas* of Mercator (1512-94) represents the results of the thorough 16th-century revision of the impression of the physical image of Europe received from antiquity. Mercator saw his enterprise as a continuation of Ptolemy's (see no. 3): he planned to make a three-volume geographical work, the first being a revised version of Ptolemy, the second a modern collection of maps, and the third a volume of notes on the differences. Only the revised Ptolemy appeared in his lifetime. He used reports of Spanish and Portuguese sailors and, in the map of the arctic region shown here, he used observations made during the expedition of Frobisher in 1576-78 and during that of Davies in 1585-87. This is the first book to have the word 'Atlas' in the title. It was named after a mythical Libyan king, following the late 16th-century fashion of giving a book first a name after a famous person and then a descriptive title. The theme of the wise monarch is developed further in the letter of dedication to Elizabeth I, Queen of England, whose contribution to geography was constituted by the information gathered by explorers. The link between exploration and political expansion is made unambiguous by Mercator, who predicted that Elizabeth's explorers had laid the foundations for English and European dominance of the entire globe.

The projection with parallel longitudes and latitudes for which Mercator is now known was designed by him in order to improve maps for navigational purposes, but the projection was too unusual to gain immediate acceptance. The map shown here, finished after Gerardus's death by his son Rummold, uses a projection in which the meridians are equally spaced straight lines, and the parallels are equally spaced circles centred at the pole. Only the centre, in this case the North Pole, is accurate, but the distortion is not excessive if the map covers one hemisphere only, and there is no distortion of the relation of the central point to any given point. As a young man, Mercator had made astronomical instruments for — among others — Charles V, the Holy Roman Emperor, and that is probably why he used this projection which had long been used in astronomical maps.

Provenance: certainly in the Bodleian by 1620, possibly from the foundation in 1602: bound by Dominique Pinart, a Frenchman who worked for Sir Thomas Bodley and his Library from 1601 to 1613.

Literature: ed. I. C. Koeman, *Atlantes Neerlandici*, vol. 2 (Amsterdam, 1969), 281-83, 295-302; S. Gibson, *Early Oxford Bindings* (Oxford Bibliographical Society Illustrated Monographs 10: Oxford, 1903), rolls XII and XVIII: this copy not listed.

Arch. B b.12 (map 5)

Sep: tentrio: nalium Terrarum de: scriptio.
Per Gerardum Mercatorem. Cum Privilegio
California regio sola fama Hispanis nota
Oceanus Scythicus qui et Mare Tabin
Polus Arcticus
Oceanus Septen
Mare gla
Scetland insulae
Farre in: sulae
Anian regnum
Bergi regio
Desertum de Belgian

Shaping the World

Pilgrimage

5 William Wey, *Itineraries*.
Edington, Wiltshire; *c*.1470.
105 leaves; 235 x 170 mm.

In the days before tourism and annual holidays, pilgrimage provided an important motive and opportunity for travel. Its basis was the belief that the places associated with the life of Christ, and the bodies of the saints, could act as channels for the holiness and power of those already in Heaven. Thus it made sense to go to Jerusalem, or Rome, or Compostela in northern Spain (where the Apostle James, son of Zebedee, was believed to be buried), or to a shrine of more local importance, as an act of devotion or penitence, or to seek help or healing. The ecclesiastical proprietors of such sites and relics promoted the practice, since pilgrims contributed to their spiritual prestige and material well-being. It was not only the poor and uneducated who believed in the efficacy of such journeys: William Wey had been a Fellow of Exeter College, Oxford and of Eton, before entering the August-inian priory of Edington. But the practice had its critics: some argued that pilgrims were motivated more by curiosity and a sense of adventure than by piety; that wealth was squandered in the construction of precious reliquaries designed to attract more wealth; and, since the spiritual journey was preferable to the physical, that pilgrims should be urged to pursue holy lives, not holy places.

Wey went on three pilgrimages — to Santiago de Compostela in 1456, and twice to Jerusalem, in 1458 and 1462. The trips to Jerusalem each lasted a little less than forty weeks. Here he describes the routes he took, and what he saw. He has an eye for detail, whether it be the celebration of the feast of St. Mark in Venice or the song sung by children begging for money in Spain. He also gives practical advice about medical matters, rates of currency exchange, the purchase of bedding, and translation into Greek. The page reproduced shows the beginning of the section in which he lists ten reasons for going on pilgrimage. Foremost amongst them are indulgences: according to Wey, pilgrims to Compostela would receive the remission of a third of all their sins; if a pilgrim died on the journey in a penitent spirit, all his or her sins would be forgiven. But the abuses of the system were open to satire: Chaucer's Pardoner is a travelling salesman, selling the benefit of relics such as pigs' bones, and a pillowcase advertised as the veil of the Virgin Mary, to people unable or unwilling to travel to a shrine themselves.

Provenance: bequeathed by Wey (d.1476) to the Chapel of the Holy Sepulchre at Edington; perhaps given to the Bodleian by 'Master Tempest', 1624.

Literature: [ed. B. Bandinel], *The Itineraries of William Wey...* (Roxburghe Club 75/1: London, 1857); SC 2351.

MS. Bodl. 565 (fol. 17r)

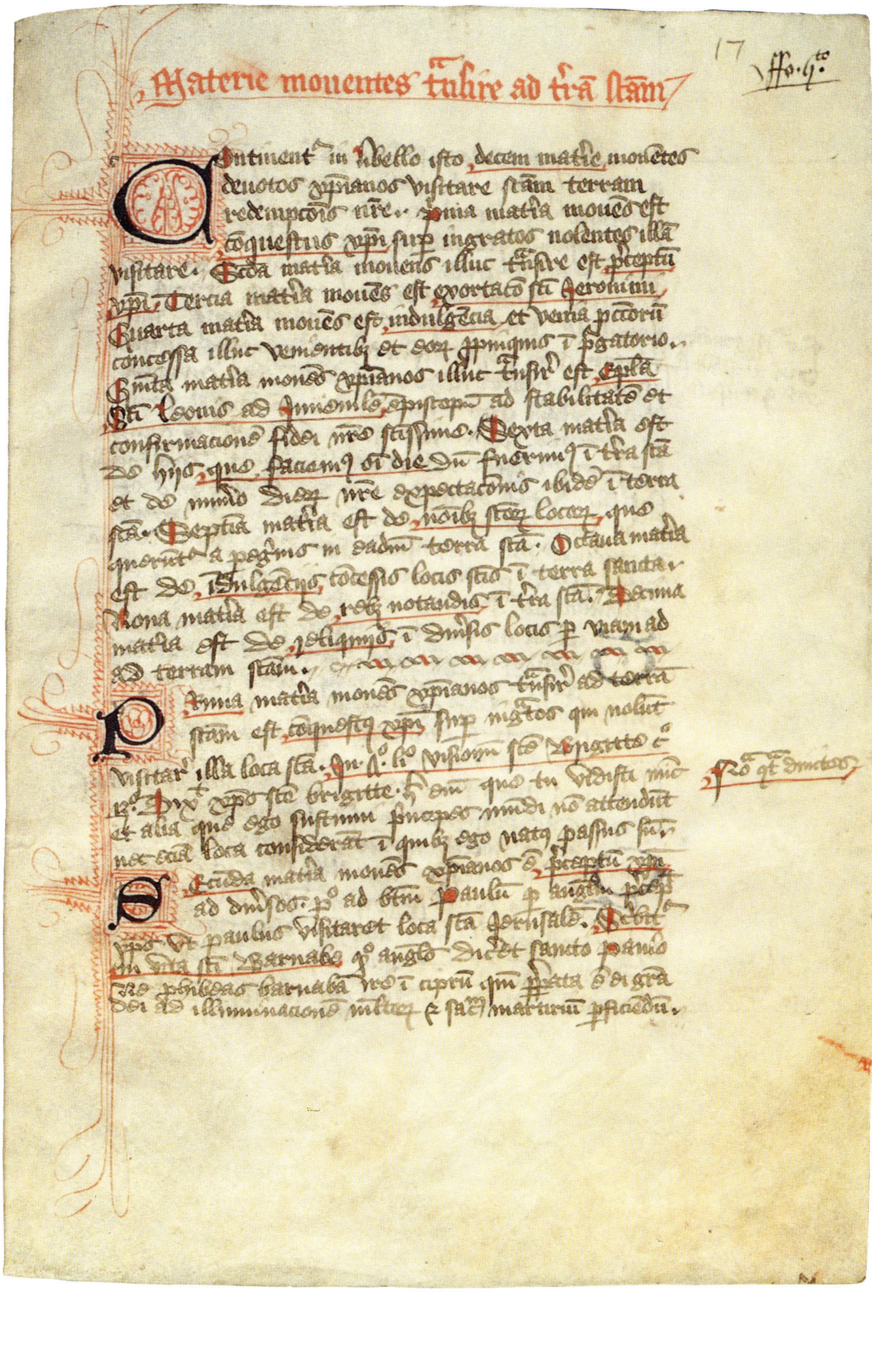

17 ffo. q.to

Materie mouentes transire ad terram sanctam

Continentur in libello isto decem materie mouentes
deuotos xpianos visitare sanctam terram
redempcionis nostre. Prima materia mouens est
conquestus xpi super ingratos nolentes illa
visitare. Secunda materia mouens illuc transire est preceptum
xpi. Tercia materia mouens est exortacio sancti Ieronimi.
Quarta materia mouens est indulgencia et venia peccatorum
concessa illuc venientibus et [illegible] in purgatorio.
Quinta materia mouens xpianos illuc transire est epistola
sancti Leonis ad [illegible] episcopum ad stabilitatem et
confirmacionem fidei nostre sanctissime. Sexta materia est
de hijs que facimus et die dum fuerimus in terra sancta
et de modo [illegible] nostre expectacionis ibidem in terra
sancta. Septima materia est de nominibus sanctorum locorum que
inueniuntur a peregrinis in eadem terra sancta. Octaua materia
est de indulgencijs concessis locis sanctis in terra sancta.
Nona materia est de rebus notandis in terra sancta. Decima
materia est de reliquijs in diuersis locis per viam ad
terram sanctam.

Prima materia mouens xpianos transire ad terram
sanctam est conquestus xpi super ingratos qui nolunt
visitare illa loca sancta. Unde in quarto libro reuelacionum sancte Brigitte c[?] — Primo est deuotos
12. Dixit xpus sancte Brigitte. Ego sum quem tu vidisti in
[illegible] et alia que ego sustinui propter [illegible] mundi non attendit
nec eciam loca considerat in quibus ego natus passus fui.
Secunda materia mouens xpianos est preceptum xpi
ad discipulos. Primo ad beatum Paulum per angelum precepit
ut Paulus visitaret loca sancta Ierusalem. [illegible]
[illegible] in vita sancti Barnabe quod angelus dixit sancto Paulo
[illegible] Paulus et Barnaba [illegible] in Ciprum [illegible] gracia
dei ad illuminacionem [illegible] et [illegible] martirium [illegible].

A Pilgrim Map of the Holy Land

6 Map of the Holy Land.
England; second half of the 14th century.
2130 x 415 mm.

In the manuscript of his pilgrim itineraries (no. 5), William Wey gives a list of places marked on 'Mappa mea de Terra Sancta', followed by a list entitled 'Distancie locorum in Terra Sancta'. The discovery in the 19th century of a close correspondence between the distances from place to place given by Wey, and those in the table with the same heading on this map, led to the conclusion that this was the very map he was describing - though the discrepancy in date means that it cannot originally have been made for him. It remains a possibility that he owned it (though it did not reach the Bodleian with his own book). However, the correspondence of places is not exact: some entries on the map are not found in Wey's list, and those that are do not always come in the same order. The general similarity might be nothing more than that which might be found between two different modern travel guides to the same destination.

Provenance: bequeathed to the Bodleian by Francis Douce (1757-1834).

Literature: *Map of the Holy Land, Illustrating the Itineraries of William Wey, Fellow of Eton in A.D. 1458 and 1462* (Roxburghe Club 75/2: London, 1867); SC 21964; P & A iii, no. 751.

MS. Douce 389

The map itself extends from Damascus in the north (on the left) to the Dead Sea, Hebron, and Beersheba in the south. The sea coast runs along the lower edge from Sidon to Gaza. Mountains and plains are green; lakes, rivers, and seas are blue. Fish swim in the Sea of Tiberias, and submerged cities are visible beneath the waters of the Dead Sea. Towns are represented by buildings and the historical figures or Biblical events associated with them: there are water-pots at Gaza, and a picture of Jacob's ladder at Bethel. Thus the map contains a good deal of information about the Holy Land in both written and visual form; but the nature of the information, as well as the size, suggests that it would have been more useful in the planning of a journey than during its progress.

Shaping the World

A Pilgrim Guide to Rome

7 *Das ist der Rom Weg.*
[Nürnberg: Erhardt Etzlaub, *c.*1494]. Single sheet; 400 x 195 mm.

Big and expensive books tend to survive better than others: they are in themselves stronger, and they tend to be owned by wealthy people or institutions who are better able to preserve them. Small books for children, cheap books for poorer people and single sheets are comparatively rare survivals. Ten copies survive of this single-sheet map of Europe, not meant for academic geographers but for practical purposes. It was probably printed first to be used by pilgrims for the holy year of 1500, when one could expect the roads of Europe to be more heavily used by people travelling to Rome. Routes begin in Cracow, Gdańsk (Danzig), Rostock, Lübeck, Marburg, Ribe, Bremen, Utrecht and Nieuwport. The map then guides the pilgrim town by town through Germany to Rome, indicating the relative positions of some 820 towns. Compared with maps in contemporary editions of Ptolemy, this is astonishingly accurate, particularly in indicating the distance between towns: each dot indicates one German mile. Borrowing a feature from Ptolemy (see no. 3), the map also shows the maximum number of daylight hours which can be expected at any latitude. Stretching from Cracow to Paris, from Edinburgh and northern Denmark to Naples, the centre of the map features Nürnberg, the place where the map was produced.

Provenance: Erwin Rosenthal, Berkeley, by 1942; acquired from Art Auctions by Albert Ehrman (1880-1969) in 1954; given to the Bodleian by John Ehrman in 1978.

Literature: H. G. Pollard, A. Ehrman, *The Distribution of Books by Catalogue* (Cambridge, 1965), fig. 9; M. von Arnim, *Bibliothek Otto Schäfer Schweinfurt* I, 1 (Stuttgart, 1984), 83; Tony Campbell, *The Earliest Printed Maps 1472-1500* (London, 1987), no. 6, pp. 59-67 (with full bibliography).

 Broxb. 95.24(1)

Mittag
Das ist der Rom weg von meylen zu meylen mit puncten verzeychnet von eyner stat zu der andern durch deutzsche lant
Das lampartisch mer
Das venedisch mer
Das pomerisch mer
Das groß deutsch mer
Schotlant
Seeland insel
Denmarck
Schon Denmarck
Der Compast
Zeelande

The Classics and Christendom

In medieval and early modern Europe the Roman Empire provided a historical framework for the notion of a transferable right to rule and for the idea of political unity. Continuity with the Empire constituted a powerful myth of political and dynastic dimensions. Charlemagne's coronation on Christmas Day 800 marked a revival of western European aspirations towards universal empire, now in a Christian guise. Later, the Holy Roman Emperors claimed to be heirs of the first Roman imperial dynasty (no. 9). The Papacy asserted itself as the successor to universal secular rule, claiming to have received the power of empire from the hands of Constantine. In 1436, some four years before Lorenzo Valla proved this claim false, a Roman cardinal had a copy made of the *Notitia dignitatum* (no. 8), a deluxe manual of imperial bureaucracy.

The importance of the pagan past for cultural and political life posed a serious moral and practical dilemma for Christian Europe. This had been a cause of anxiety for the Fathers of the Church: it was a central theme of Augustine, the bishop of Hippo, in his *De civitate Dei* (no. 18). Formal education depended on a curriculum of pagan authors: the survival of their works is in large measure due to copies made in the early Middle Ages, most often by Christian monks or the professionals they employed (no. 10). The Humanist recovery of ancient texts would not have been possible without the work of the early Middle Ages. Humanists, however, ensured that texts which had for long been inaccessible became part of public life: the recovery of a group of speeches by Cicero (no. 11) illustrates this process. The invention of printing ensured that these texts were widely distributed: mass production often necessitated a drive for export (nos 12 and 13). In the widest perspective, the dichotomy between antiquity and Christianity is less sharp. Christianity itself was part of Europe's inheritance from the ancient Mediterranean civilizations. The Laudian copy of the *Acts of the Apostles* (no. 14) — a text composed at much the same time as Pliny's *Historia naturalis* (no. 13) — written in Greek and Latin is a direct link back to the bilingual culture of pagan antiquity.

It was Christianity that provided medieval Europeans with the most potent image of their self-definition. Rulers and churchmen thought not of Europe but of 'Christendom'. This referred to the society of Latin Christians, to their faith, and to the rituals which set them apart from other peoples. Europe was a society of the baptized — to the exclusion of the Jews, who resisted efforts to conscript them to this unity, and of heretics, who threatened to corrupt it. Here we see the society of the faithful through its books: Europe as a Christian textual community. Biblical scholarship, evident already in the Laudian Acts, was concerned with both establishing and explaining the Biblical text. These were the concerns of the expanding centres of learning around cathedrals and religious houses, most importantly in 12th-century France (no. 15). Paris, the centre of learning in the high Middle Ages, also became a centre for the production of manuscript books on an increasingly commercial scale. The Gutenberg Bible (no. 16) conforms to a Parisian Bible type which gained wide currency in the later Middle Ages. In the absence of strong political authority, European unity in the early Middle Ages depended largely on the transnational structure of the Church. In the case of the religious elite of monks and nuns, it was a rule of life enshrined in a text which helped to bind together the scattered, at first largely autonomous communities (no. 17). In the period of early printing the monastic orders still had a role to play in the facilitating of cultural contacts across Europe (no. 18). Liturgy was an important unifying element, laying down how public acts of worship were to be performed throughout the Christian West. Despite regional variation, the missal from Würzburg (no. 19) shows how attempts were made, at a local level, to use the invention of printing to impose greater uniformity. Books of Hours were for private devotion, but their structure enabled lay persons to follow the daily rhythms of worship of those in holy orders (no. 20).

The Classics and Christendom

The Roman Empire

8 The *Notitia Dignitatum* (with other geographical and military texts).
Basel; 1436.
ii + 175 leaves; 275 x 195 mm.

The *Notitia Dignitatum* is a handbook of the civil and military officials of the late Roman Empire. The core of the list seems to date from *c.*395 AD, with additions up to *c.*430. The two halves of the Empire, newly divided, are treated separately: the western half is more complete. The process of updating may have made the document as difficult for contemporary officials to use as it is for modern historians, since the movement of troops led some units to be registered in more than one place.

The section of the *Notitia* devoted to each senior civilian official or military commander includes a picture of his insignia of office (usually a codicil for the civilians and a shield for the soldiers), and a statement of the sphere of competence of the post concerned, often listing its subordinates in the imperial hierarchy. The pages exhibited concern the *vicarius* of Britain, whose immediate superior was the Praetorian prefect of the Gauls. Serving the *vicarius* were the governors of the five provinces forming the diocese: the *consulares* of Maxima Caesariensis and Valentia, and the *praesides* of Flavia Caesariensis, Britannia Prima, and Britannia Secunda - perhaps based at London, York, Carlisle, Cirencester, and Lincoln respectively.

This important Roman document is known only from later copies. This, the earliest complete copy to survive, was made in 1436 for Pietro Donato, Bishop of Padua, during the Council of Basel. Donato had borrowed an earlier manuscript (perhaps of the early 10th century) from Speyer Cathedral; he employed a French illuminator, Perronet Lamy, and an Italian scribe to do the copying. Both the Late Antique original and the 10th-century intermediary are lost, though there are several other 15th- and 16th-century copies.

Provenance: Jacopo Soranzo (1686-1761); Matteo Luigi Canonici (1727-c.1806); bought by the Bodleian as part of the Canonici collection, 1817.

Literature: Quarto cat. III, col. 719; P & A i, no. 666, and ii, no. 599; *Survival of Ancient Literature* no. 146; eds. R. Goodburn, P. Bartholomew, *Aspects of the Notitia Dignitatum* (British Archaeological Reports, Supplementary Series 15: Oxford, 1976).

MS. Canon. Misc. 378
(fol. 150v)

VICARII BRITANIARVM.
FL
INTALL
COMORD
PR
Maxima Caesariensis.
Britania pma.
Valentia.
Britania secunda.
Flavia Caesariensis.

The Classics and Christendom

Spain and the Roman Emperors

9 Hubertus Goltzius, *Vivæ omnium fere imperatorum imagines a C. Iulio Cæsare usque ad Carolum V et Ferdinandum.*
Antwerp: Hubertus Goltzius Herbopolita, 1557, 2°. 155 leaves; 320 x 230 mm.

Pretensions to continuity with the empires of the past were not confined to the Papacy. Part of the Habsburg version of the imperial myth was the claim that the family descended from Aeneas, the Trojan hero and mythical ancestor of Julius Caesar. In 1556 Charles V, Holy Roman Emperor, made his son, Philip II, King of Spain, Naples and Sicily. Already Duke of Milan, he was made Duke of Flanders and also given the sovereignty of the order of the Golden Fleece — an important part of the Trojan myth — and the titular sovereignty of Jerusalem as well as the title of Byzantine Emperor: thus both the religious and the secular legitimation of his dynasty was secured. Philip was set to continue the Habsburg myth. With its new transatlantic empire, Spain had as great an interest as any European country in proving the legitimacy of the idea of empire (see also no. 54).

This collection of splendid portrait medallions of Roman Emperors — printed using a technique not yet fully understood — was dedicated to Philip, and the work serves an obvious purpose in the mythological history and the claim to universal monarchy. In addition to his Habsburg titles, Philip was addressed as King of England, because of his marriage to Mary Tudor, and therefore also King of France. The book opens with portraits of Caesar and Augustus. Some medallions of more obscure later emperors are left blank, to reinforce the impression that the existing portraits are true likenesses of the imperial ancestors. The book ends with portraits of Charles and his brother Ferdinand, the future Emperor of the Holy Roman Empire, and a final double portrait of Philip himself with his cousin Maximilian, Ferdinand's son, King of Bohemia and future Roman Emperor, an emblem of the concord between the two Habsburg branches. Goltzius (1526–83) produced the book in the prosperous Flemish trading city of Antwerp, then part of the Spanish empire, and was careful to stress his Roman Catholic attitudes. His close link with imperial historiography is further illustrated by his *Caius Iulius Cæsar* (Bruges, 1563), another numismatic work: the Bodleian copy of this is in a dedication binding from Goltzius to Philip of Spain.

Provenance: Philipp Carteret Webb, MP, FSA (1700–70), inter alia collector of coins and medals; sale 25 February 1771; bequeathed to the Bodleian by Francis Douce (1757–1834).

Douce G subt. 7 (fols. 19v–20r)

.I.

SATIVS EST SEMEL MORI, QVAM ASSIDVA SPE ET EXPECTATIONE VITAM PERDERE.

Anno imperij .v., ætatis verò .LVI. inopinata cæde oppressus periit.

A 2

The Classics and Christendom

Monastic Copies of the Classics

10 Terence, *Comedies*.
St. Albans; mid-12th century.
iv + 181 leaves; 285 x 215 mm.

The works of the pagan authors of classical antiquity copied in the early Middle Ages by Christian monks (or the professionals they employed) were not in general lavishly illustrated or decorated; Terence is an exception. The illustrations depict the masks and exaggerated gestures of the Roman stage: the page reproduced (from the beginning of the book) shows the empty masks to be used in the first play, the *Andria*; on the other side of the opening, an 'author portrait' is supported by actors wearing two of the masks. The cycle of illustrations (representing all the characters of each scene) was Late Antique (late 4th or early 5th century AD) in origin. The close copying of each individual composition in the chain of surviving manuscripts runs parallel with radical changes of artistic style: here the original sketchy three-dimensionality has been replaced by the firm outlines and stylized draperies of the Romanesque. This marks the close of the classicizing, 'antiquarian' tradition of illustration. The plays of Terence were still popular in the Gothic period, but in the illustrations (if any) the characters take on the guise of Gothic knights and ladies.

This manuscript was probably made at the abbey of St. Albans by itinerant professional scribes and artists. Four artists worked on the illustrations: the first has been identified as the 'Master of the Apocrypha Drawings', known as such from his work in a great Bible produced at Winchester (now in the Cathedral Library). He may have been the leader of a team, working in France as well as England. It has been argued that the chief exemplar was a Carolingian manuscript now in Paris (Bibliothèque Nationale, MS. lat. 7899); but there must in fact have been more than one parent, and the key may lie in the Terence 'industry' active at Tours in the early 12th century.

Provenance: perhaps the Terence given as a bribe by the abbot of St. Albans to Richard de Bury, Keeper of the Privy Seal 1329-33; Roger Walle, Archdeacon of Coventry (d.1488); Henry Allen; Sir William Cavendish (d.1577); Nicholas Frevile of Hardwick, Co. Durham (d.1674); by descent to Frevile Lambton; given by him to the Bodleian, 1704.

Literature: SC 27603; L.W. Jones, C.R. Morey, *The Miniatures of the Manuscripts of Terence prior to the Thirteenth Century* (Princeton, 1931); P & A iii, no. 132; R.M. Thomson, *Manuscripts from St. Albans Abbey 1066-1235* (2 vols: Woodbridge, 1982), no. 41; B. Munk Olsen, *L'Étude des auteurs classiques latins aux XIe et XIIe siècles*, II (Paris, 1985), 623-4; J.N. Grant, *Studies in the Textual Tradition of Terence* (Toronto, 1986).

MS. Auct. F. 2. 13 (fol. 3r)

The Classics and Christendom

Humanist Rediscoveries

11 Cicero, *Orationes*.
Florence; 1418.
iv + 125 leaves; 245 x 165 mm.

The circumstances of this book's production give it an exemplary place in the history of the early Italian Humanists' search for the texts of classical authors not available to them. The speeches of Cicero it contains were rediscovered by Poggio Bracciolini in the autumn of 1417, probably at Cologne and Langres, during the period of his employment as papal *scriptor* at the Council of Constance. Poggio sent the copy he had made (now Vatican City, Bibliotheca Apostolica Vaticana, Vat. lat. 11458) to his friend and fellow-enthusiast Niccolò Niccoli in Florence, where this and other copies were made. By August 1418 Poggio's manuscript was in the hands of Francesco Barbaro in Venice.

The hand of the Bodleian manuscript can be identified as that of Giovanni Aretino (Ser Giovanni di Cenni, Chancellor of Arezzo in 1410-11), one of Poggio's earliest and most accomplished followers in the practice of Humanist script. Based on the late Carolingian minuscule of the manuscripts in which the Humanists discovered classical and other texts, Humanistic script represented a return to the ideal of antique clarity. The restrained initials, consisting of white entwined vinestems against a coloured ground, were derived from the initials of 12th-century Italian manuscripts, and also represent a reaction against the exuberance of Gothic forms.

On the page exhibited, in the gap between the end of one speech and the beginning of another, Richard Hunt discovered the semi-erased ex-libris of Cosimo de' Medici: its position had presumably been intended to avoid the fate which did in fact befall it. The discovery was not in itself surprising: Aretino wrote other books for Cosimo, who was advised by Niccoli in his efforts to build up a classical library. Together with the books of his son and grandson, Cosimo's library was to form the core of the collection of the Biblioteca Laurenziana in Florence.

Provenance: Cosimo 'il Vecchio' de' Medici, 1418; alienated from the Medici collection, perhaps already in the 15th or 16th century? (not in any inventory of the Medici library); Anton Maria Biscioni, *Bibliotecario* of the Laurenziana 1741- 56, by 1740; J.P. D'Orville, Dutch classicist, 1746; bought by the Bodleian with the rest of the D'Orville collection in 1804.

Literature: SC 16956; P & A ii, no. 211; M.C. Davies, 'A Note on the History of MS. D'Orville 78', BLR 11 (1982-5), 253-8; A.C. de la Mare, 'Cosimo and his Books', in *Cosimo 'il Vecchio' de' Medici 1389-1464*, ed. F. Ames-Lewis (Oxford, 1992), 115-56, pp. 128, 144 no. 29.

 MS. D'Orville 78 (fol. 26r)

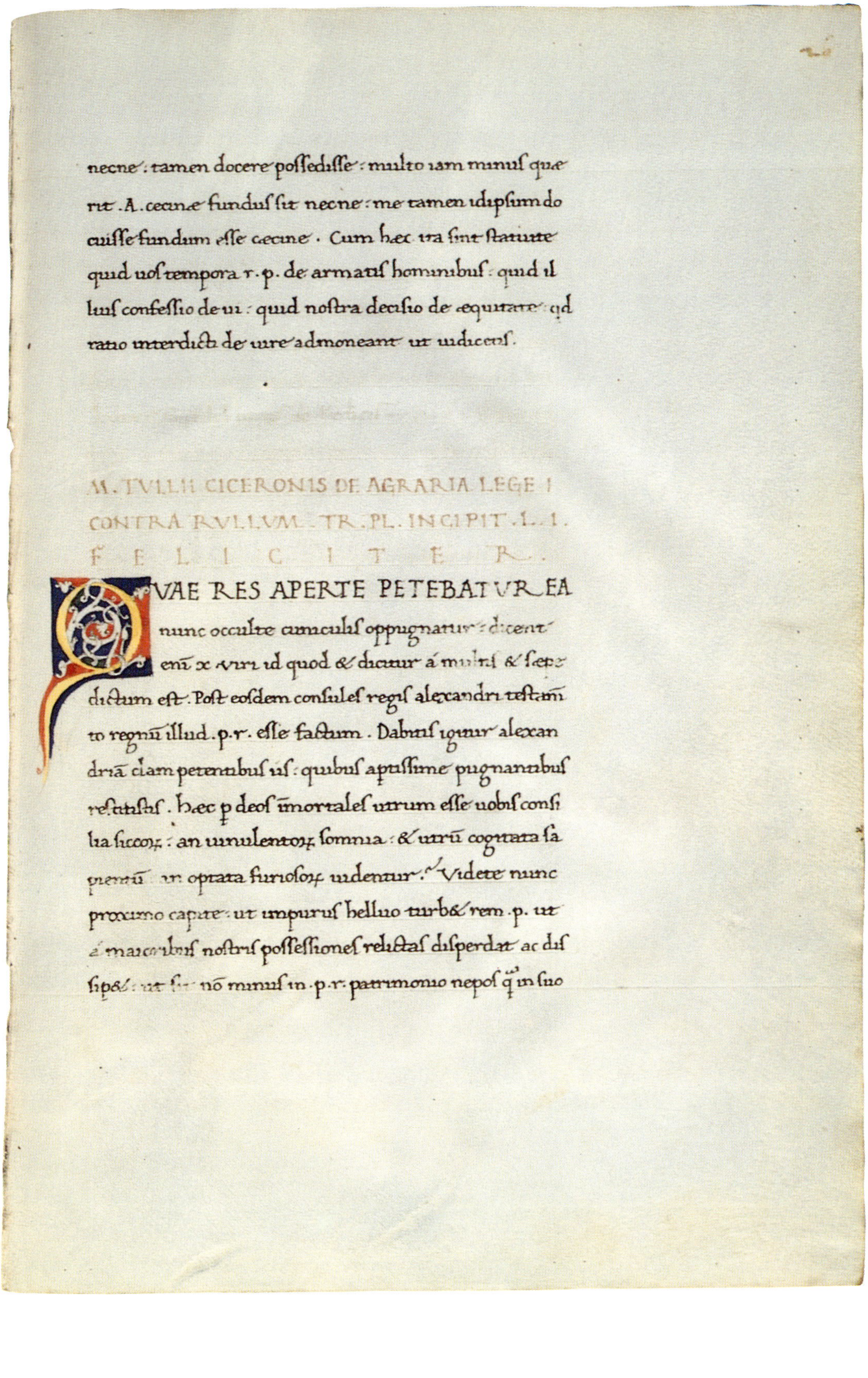
necne: tamen docere possedisse: multo iam minus quaerit. A. cecinae fundus sit necne: me tamen idipsum docuisse fundum esse cecinae. Cum haec ita sint statuite quid uos tempora r.p. de armatis hominibus: quid illius confessio de ui: quid nostra decisio de aequitate: quid ratio interdicti de iure admoneant ut iudicetis.

M. TULLII CICERONIS DE AGRARIA LEGE I
CONTRA RULLUM TR. PL. INCIPIT. L. I.
F E L I C I T E R.

QUAE RES APERTE PETEBATUR EA nunc occulte cuniculis oppugnatur: dicent enim x viri id quod et dicitur a multis et saepe dictum est. Post eosdem consules regis alexandri testamento regnum illud p.r. esse factum. Dabitis igitur alexandriam clam petentibus iis: quibus apertissime pugnantibus restitistis. haec per deos immortales utrum esse uobis consilia siccorum: an uinulentorum somnia: et utrum cogitata sapientium: an optata furiosorum uidentur. Videte nunc proximo capite: ut impurus helluo turbet rem p. ut a maioribus nostris possessiones relictas disperdat ac dissipet: ut sit non minus in p.r. patrimonio nepos quam in suo

The Classics and Christendom

First Editions and Pirated Editions

12 Titus Livius, *Ab urbe condita*.
Venice: Wendelin von Speyer, 1470, 2°. 2 vols, 421 leaves; 390 x 265 mm.

Rome was the first major centre of printing in Italy, but it was soon overtaken by Venice. There printers could obtain financial backing from merchants and bankers with international commercial connections which provided an opportunity for the systematic exportation of printed books. Venice was, therefore, in a much better position to exploit the new opportunity for mass production of books than any other city in Europe (see no. 13). Classical texts first printed in Rome were soon reprinted in Venice. Thus, Livy was first printed in Rome in 1469 while the edition shown here is the Venetian 'pirated' edition. Already in the 1470s classical texts were produced in Venice in such numbers that it has been argued that oversupply resulted in a crisis for the Venetian printing industry.

This copy of Wendelin's edition of Livy displays how experiments were made with the mass production of elements which were otherwise finished by hand. The glorious Renaissance borders look like individual, handmade paintings, but are in fact painted over woodcuts which have been stamped onto the page in a separate process after the printing of the text. The two centaurs with putti on their backs at the foot of the page are, however, not painted over woodcuts. Nonetheless, a similar monster is found in a Cicero also printed by Wendelin in 1470, now in the Fitzwilliam Museum in Cambridge: probably the same pattern was used. Both the woodcut and the drawing are by an artist named by Armstrong the 'Master of the Putti'. It seems probable that these experiments with mass-produced decorations took place in his workshop rather than in Wendelin's.

Provenance: the Venetian family of Dolfin;'F O 1632', possibly Francesco, conte di Onigo; probably Maffeo Pinelli (1735-85): see Jacobus Morellius, *Bibliotheca Maphæi Pinellii Veneti magno jam studio collecta* (Venice, 1787), no. 2823; bought by the Bodleian at the Pinelli sale in 1790.

Literature: P & A ii, no. pr. 59; L. Armstrong, *Renaissance Miniature Painters and Classical Imagery; The Master of the Putti and his Venetian Workshop* (London,1981), no. 4.

Auct. L 1.9 (fol. 172r: vol. 2, fol. 1r)

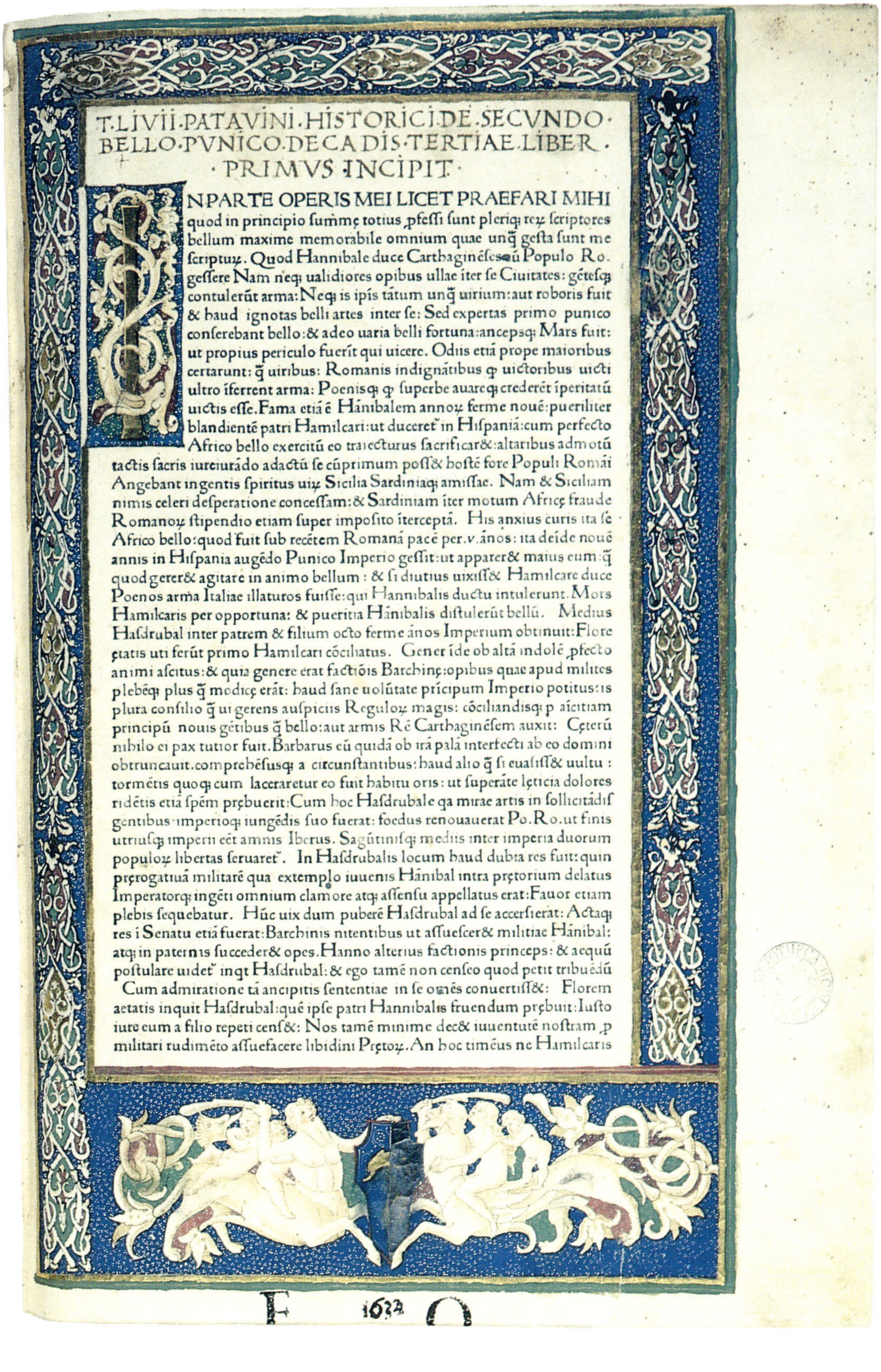

T·LIVII·PATAVINI·HISTORICI·DE·SECVNDO·BELLO·PVNICO·DECADIS·TERTIAE·LIBER·PRIMVS·INCIPIT·

IN PARTE OPERIS MEI LICET PRAEFARI MIHI quod in principio summę totius ꝓfessi sunt pleriq; reꝝ scriptores bellum maxime memorabile omnium quae unq̃ gesta sunt me scriptuꝝ. Quod Hannibale duce Carthaginẽses cũ Populo Ro. gessere Nam neq; ualidiores opibus ullae iter se Ciuitates: gẽtesq; contulerũt arma: Neq; is ipis tãtum unq̃ uirium: aut roboris fuit & haud ignotas belli artes inter se: Sed expertas primo punico conserebant bello: & adeo uaria belli fortuna: ancepsq; Mars fuit: ut propius periculo fuerit qui uicere. Odiis etiã prope maioribus certarunt: q̃ uiribus: Romanis indignãtibus ꝙ uictoribus uicti ultro ĩferrent arma: Poenisq; ꝙ superbe auareq; crederẽt ĩperitatũ uictis esse. Fama etiã ẽ Hãnibalem annoꝝ ferme nouẽ: pueriliter blandientẽ patri Hamilcari: ut duceret̃ in Hispaniã: cum perfecto Africo bello exercitũ eo traiecturus sacrificar&: altaribus admotũ tactis sacris iureiurãdo adactũ se cũprimum poss& hostẽ fore Populi Romãi Angebant ingentis spiritus uiꝝ Sicilia Sardiniaq; amissae. Nam & Siciliam nimis celeri desperatione concessam: & Sardiniam ĩter motum Africę fraude Romanoꝝ stipendio etiam super imposito ĩterceptã. His anxius curis ita se Africo bello: quod fuit sub recẽtem Romanã pacẽ per. v. ãnos: ita deide nouẽ annis in Hispania augẽdo Punico Imperio gessit: ut apparer& maius eum: q̃ quod gerer& agitare in animo bellum: & si diutius uixiss& Hamilcare duce Poenos arma Italiae illaturos fuisse: qui Hannibalis ductu intulerunt. Mors Hamilcaris per opportuna: & pueritia Hãnibalis distulerũt bellũ. Medius Hasdrubal inter patrem & filium octo ferme ãnos Imperium obtinuit: Flore ętatis uti ferũt primo Hamilcari cõciliatus. Gener ĩde ob altã indolẽ ꝓfecto animi ascitus: & quia genere erat factiõis Barchinę: opibus quae apud milites plebẽq; plus q̃ modicę erãt: haud sane uolũtate prĩcipum Imperio potitus: is plura consilio q̃ ui gerens auspiciis Reguloꝝ magis: cõciliandisq; ꝑ aĩcitiam principũ nouis gẽtibus q̃ bello: aut armis Rẽ Carthaginẽsem auxit: Cęterũ nihilo ei pax tutior fuit. Barbarus eũ quidã ob irã palã interfecti ab eo domini obtruncauit. comprehẽsusq; a circunstantibus: haud alio q̃ si euasiss& uultu: tormẽtis quoq; cum lacceraretur eo fuit habitu oris: ut superãte lęticia dolores ridẽtis etiã spẽm prębuerit: Cum hoc Hasdrubale q̃a mirae artis in sollicitãdis gentibus imperioq; iungẽdis suo fuerat: foedus renouauerat Po. Ro. ut finis utriusq; imperii eẽt amnis Iberus. Sagũtinisq; mediis inter imperia duorum populoꝝ libertas seruaret̃. In Hasdrubalis locum haud dubia res fuit: quin pręrogatiuã militarẽ qua extemplo iuuenis Hãnibal intra pętorium delatus Imperatorq; ingẽti omnium clamore atq; assensu appellatus erat: Fauor etiam plebis sequebatur. Hũc uix dum puberẽ Hasdrubal ad se accersierat: Actaq; res ĩ Senatu etiã fuerat: Barchinis nitentibus ut assuescer& militiae Hãnibal: atq; in paternis succeder& opes. Hanno alterius factionis princeps: & aequũ postulare uidet̃ inq̃t Hasdrubal: & ego tamẽ non censeo quod petit tribuẽdũ Cum admiratione tã ancipitis sententiae in se omẽs conuertiss&: Florem aetatis inquit Hasdrubal: quẽ ipse patri Hannibalis fruendum prębuit: Iusto iure eum a filio repeti cens&: Nos tamẽ minime dec& iuuentutẽ nostram ꝓ militari rudimẽto assuefacere libidini Pręroꝝ. An hoc timẽus ne Hamilcaris

The Classics and Christendom

Classics for Export

13 Gaius Plinius Secundus, *Historia naturalis*.
Venice: Johannes von Speyer, 1469, 2°. 356 leaves; 410 x 270 mm.

In his description of natural phenomena, Pliny the elder (*c*.23-79 AD) drew on many Roman and Greek authorities since lost, and his monumental work became the comprehensive encyclopedia of ancient knowledge. Although he died during the eruption of Vesuvius and never finished the work, it formed the basis for smaller collections of excerpts and, in the Middle Ages, his work was most frequently known through such compilations. Italian Humanists, already in the 14th century, began to show new interest in the work. As with other classical texts, many manuscripts which were used by Humanists came from north of the Alps (see also Cicero's orations, no. 11). One Pliny manuscript was brought to Italy from as far away as Lübeck. To understand and, often, to reject Pliny's text, was important for students of the natural world. Only by establishing a firm terminology could a common European scientific language be formed. Pliny's importance was great in the field of terminology for animals, plants, minerals, stones, and man-made instruments. Without Pliny, it would have been impossible to use a classical Latin terminology for scientific purposes; but it could be difficult to attach his vocabulary to specific things. J. C. Scaliger, a 16th-century scholar, said, 'Instead of giving us a meal, he provides us with the menu only': fleshing out Pliny's words became the task of scientists (see no. 25). The first edition of Pliny was printed by Johannes von Speyer, a German immigrant and the first printer in Venice. Johannes's brother, Wendelin, wrote that it took three months to print 100 copies. When, in 1471, Sigismund Rechlinger wrote to the associates of Wendelin about books which he had failed to sell in Nürnberg, Pliny's *History* was a book for which he said he would be able to find German buyers. Our copy was exported to Bavaria shortly after being printed: the hand-painted decoration is South German, and incorporates the coat of arms of the Bavarian Upfkofer family. Shown here is the opening of book one: the first leaf is a parchment replacement with the text written in a German hand, imitating the typeface, itself an imitation of Italian Humanist handwriting — an unusual illustration of the way in which printing contributed to the diffusion of Humanist handwriting, still not common north of the Alps. Perhaps the first leaf had been damaged in the transport from Venice to Bavaria or, alternatively, Upfkofer had a parchment leaf inserted in order to enhance the impression of luxury.

Provenance: late 15th century: Upfkofer, Bavarian noble family; acquired by Edward Harley from Nathaniel Noel, the London bookseller, shortly before 17 April 1722; in the Bodleian by 1795.

Literature: eds. C. E. and R. C. Wright, *The Diary of Humfrey Wanley* (Oxford, 1966), vol. 1, 138; M. Cortesi, 'Incunaboli Veneziani in Germania', in *Vestigia. Studi in onore di Giuseppe Billanovich, I* (Rome, 1984), 197-219.

Auct. L 1.1 (fol. 1r)

Vita Plinii ex cathalago Virorum illustrium tranquilli. Incipit:
PLINIUS secundus nouocomensis equestribus militiis industrie functus: procuratio
nes quoq; splendidissimas atq; continuas summa integritate administrauit. Et tamen
liberalibus studiis tantam operam dedit: ut non temere quis plura in ocio scripserit. Itaque
bella omnia que undiq; cum romanis gesta sunt. xxxvii. uoluminibus comprehendit. Item
naturalis historie. xxxvii. libros absoluit. Periit cladis campanie. Nam cum misenensi
classi preesset & flagrante Vesevo: ad explorandas propius causas liburnicas pretendisset: ne
q; aduersantibus uentis remeare posset: ui pulueris ac fauille oppressus est: uel ut quidam
existimant a seruo suo occisus: que deficiens estu ut necem sibi maturaret orauerat. Hic in his
libris. xx. milia rerum dignarum ex lectione uoluminum circiter duum milium complexus est.
Primus autem liber qui index. xxxvii. librorum sequentium est suo ac totius operis & speciem continet titulorum.

Cayus Plinius secundus naturalis hystoriae. Domiciano Imperatori. S. P. D.

LIBROS NATVRALIS HISTORIAE
nouicium camenis quiritium tuorum opus natum apud me
proxima fetura licenciore epistola narrare constitui
tibi iocundissime imperator. Sit enim hec tui prefacio
uerissima: dum maxime consenescit in patre. Nam
que tu solebas putare esse aliquid meas nugas:
ut obiicere moliar. Catullum conterraneum meum
agnoscis & hoc castrense uerbum: ille enim ut scis per
mutatis prioribus sillabis duriusculum se fecit
quam uolebat existimari a uernaculis tuis & famulis.
Simul ut hac mea petulancia fiat quod proxime non
fieri questus es in alia procaci epistola nostra ut in
quedam acta exeant. Sciantq; omnes quam ex equo
tecum uiuat imperium triumphalis & censorius tu
sexiesq; consul ac tribunicie potestatis particeps: et
quod iis nobilius fecisti: dum illud patri pariter & eques
tri ordini prestas prefectus pretorii eius omniaq;
hec rei publice: et nobis quidem qualis in castrensi contubernio. Nec quicquam mutauit in te fortune
amplitudo in his: nisi ut prodesse tantundem posses ut uelles. Itaq; cum ceteris in ueneracionem
tui pateant omnia illa: nobis ad colendum te familiarius audacia sola superest. Hanc igitur tibi
imputabis: et in nostra culpa tibi ignosces. Perfricui faciem: nec tamen profeci quoniam alia
uia occurris: ingens & longius eciam summoues ingenii fascibus fulgurat in nullo unquam
uerius dicta uis eloquencie tribunicie potestatis facundie. quanto tu ore patris laudes tonas:
quanto fratris amas: quantus in poetica es. O magna fecunditas animi quemadmodum fratrem quoq;
imitareris excogitasti: sed hec quis posset intrepidus extimare subiturus ingenii tui iudicium
presertim lacessitum. Neq; enim similis est condicio publicantium & nominatim tibi dicancium:
Tum possem dicere quid ista legis imperator humili uulgo scripta sunt agricolarum opificum
turbe denique studiorum ociosis quid te iudicem facis: quia hanc operam cum dicerem non eras in
hoc albo: maiorem te sciebam quam ut descensurum huc putarem. Preterea est quedam
publica eciam eruditorum reiectio: utitur illa: et M. Tullius extra omnem ingenii aliam positus
et quod miremur per aduocatum defenditur nec doctissimum omnium. Persium hoc legere uolo.
Lelium Congium uolo. Quod si hoc Lucilius qui primus condidit stili nasum legerit quasi
abusionem & uituperacionem reputabit: primus enim satyricum carmen conscripsit in quo
utiq; uituperacio uniuscuiusq; continetur. Nasum autem dixit quasi uituperacionis signum uel
maxime naso declarandum dicendumq; est: si aduocatum sibi putauit. Cicero mutuandum
presertim cum de republica scriberet quanto nos cautius ab aliquo iudice defendimur

The Classics and Christendom

The Bible in Latin and Greek

14 The Laudian *Acts of the Apostles*.
Sardinia?; late 6th or early 7th century.
iii + 230 leaves; 265 x 215 mm.

The Laudian Acts is Oxford's most important Biblical manuscript, a witness to the continuing bilingualism of the Mediterranean world, a monument to English learning in the age of Bede, a relic of Anglo-Saxon evangelizing activity in Germany, and a refugee from the Thirty Years' War. The text is written in parallel columns, Latin on the left, Greek on the right, with only one or two words to a line: both were written by the same scribe in closely-related uncial scripts. Flyleaf inscriptions at the end suggest that he may have been working in a Greek religious house on the island of Sardinia. The opening reproduced contains the Ethiopian eunuch's confession of faith at Acts 8.37 as part of the main text, the earliest surviving Greek manuscript to do so.

Close analysis of the text has given rise to a hypothesis about the next stage of the manuscript's history. Bede, in his two commentaries on Acts, used (amongst others) a bilingual version whose pre-Vulgate Latin text corresponds to the wording found in this manuscript and no other. Bede never left England, but books were imported from Rome to Wearmouth/Jarrow by Benedict Biscop and others: either this manuscript or a lost twin must have been amongst them. In his *Historia Ecclesiastica*, Bede asserts that there are still students of Theodore of Tarsus (died 690) in England 'who know Latin and Greek just as well as their native tongue': but there is little other evidence for the existence of Greek texts in England at this time. Indeed, this manuscript itself did not remain in England. It was eventually acquired by the agents of Archbishop Laud in Germany in 1636, in the wake of the dispersal of the library of St. Kylian's Cathedral, Würzburg by the Swedish army in the Thirty Years' War. St. Kylian's had been founded by St. Boniface in 741. A list of books added *c.*800 in an Anglo-Saxon hand to another Laudian manuscript (MS. Laud Misc. 126) probably refers to the library of St. Kylian's; it gives pride of place to a manuscript of the Acts of the Apostles, suggesting that the Laudian Acts might have reached Germany early on in the baggage of an Anglo-Saxon missionary.

Provenance: bought in Germany in 1636 for Archbishop Laud and given in his third major donation to Oxford University, 1639.

Literature: Quarto cat. I, col. 517; ed. C. Tischendorf, *Codex Laudianus*... (Monumenta Sacra Inedita 9 (Novae Collectionis Appendix): Leipzig, 1870); E.A. Lowe, 'An Eighth-Century List of Books in a Bodleian MS. from Würzburg and its Probable Relation to the Laudian Acts', *Speculum* 3 (1928), 3-15; M.L.W. Laistner, 'The Latin Versions of Acts Known to the Venerable Bede', *Harvard Theological Review* 30 (1937), 37-50; CLA ii, no. 251.

MS. Laud Gr. 35 (fols. 70v-71r)

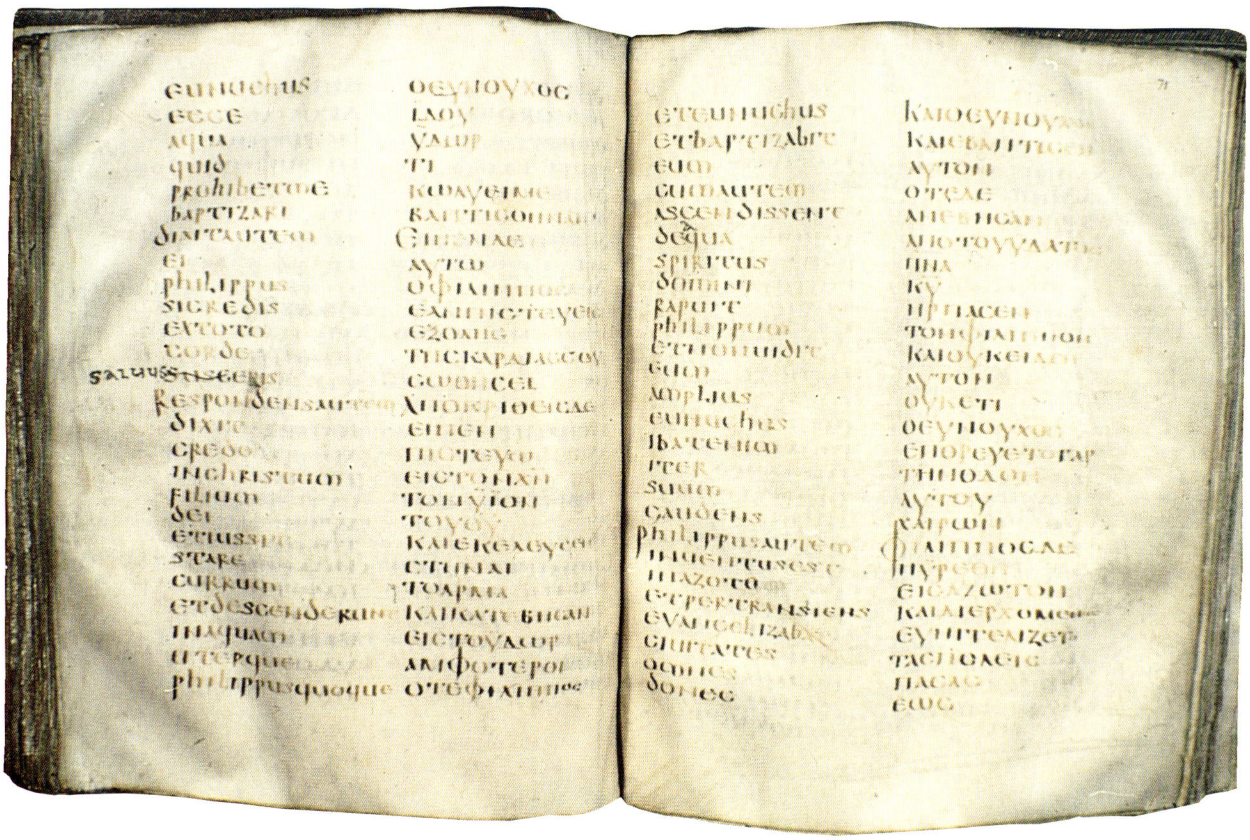

The Glossed Bible

15 Glossed *Gospel of St. John.*
Paris; mid-12th century.
i + 125 leaves; 240 x 160 mm.

The practice of glossing the text of the Bible must have begun as an informal process by which teachers and preachers wrote marginal and interlinear notes and Biblical cross-references around the text. The interpretations themselves were not new: the process was one of distilling and arranging the commentaries of the Church Fathers. The surviving evidence for this activity in the West goes back to the Carolingian period: work seems to have intensified in the burgeoning cathedral schools of France in the late 11th and early 12th centuries. Glossed versions of the various books of the Bible circulated separately: the Psalter, Pauline Epistles, and Gospel of St. John were amongst the earliest to gain popularity. By the 1140s, complete sets of glossed books of the Bible were being produced; and in the second half of the century, they were acquired in large numbers by religious houses in all parts of Europe. The centre of 'publication' was Paris.

This manuscript is one of the best-preserved examples of Romanesque blind-stamped binding. The upper and lower covers display different designs, the patterns made up of rows of impressions of various engraved metal dies in the tanned leather. Very unusually, the original fastening also survives. Over half of the surviving examples of these bindings cover glossed books of the Bible: many share the same motifs. The binders were evidently closely associated with the process of production of the glossed books. The texts of the manuscripts thus copied and bound in Paris were often left undecorated, no doubt in the expectation that initials would be filled in at their destinations. In this case, the book was taken back to the abbey of Admont in Austria, where it remained until the 20th century; in common with many other such books, the decoration was never completed. From the 1160s-70s, decoration too was increasingly provided in Paris, by professional illuminators. But the gradual replacement of monastic and cathedral book production by lay professionals also saw the demise of the stamped binding, and the technique was not to regain popularity until the 15th century.

Provenance: Admont abbey; Lucius Wilmerding, New York 1934 (acquired through E.P. Goldschmidt); Albert Ehrman, 1951; given to the Bodleian by John Ehrman, 1979.

Literature: H.M. Nixon, *Broxbourne Library. Styles and Designs of Bookbindings from the Twelfth to the Twentieth Century* (London, 1956), no. 1; C.F.R. de Hamel, *Glossed Books of the Bible and the Origins of the Paris Book-trade* (Woodbridge, 1984), 64-86; F.A. Schmidt-Künsemüller, *Die abendländischen romanischen Blindstempeleinbände* (Denkmäler der Buchkunst 6: Stuttgart,1985), no. 11.

MS. Broxbourne 83.1 (lower cover)

The Classics and Christendom

The Gutenberg Bible

16 Biblia Latina.
[Mainz: J. Gutenberg and J. Fust, *c.*1455], 2°. 2 vols, 643 leaves; 400 x 285 mm.

Johann Gutenberg, a goldsmith (*c.*1397-1468), had worked on his invention of printing with movable type for many years, and had experimented with smaller productions, before it came to fruition in the work shown here. It is not by chance that the first substantial book printed in Europe was a Bible. Although the Bible in the Vulgate Latin translation did not constitute a completely uniform body of texts, it was the book which could give to those who experimented with mass production the best hope of producing something which they would be able to sell throughout Europe. In respect to the texts which it contained and the order in which they occurred, the Gutenberg Bible was of a Parisian type, which had most international currency in Europe north of the Alps from the 13th century. Later other northern European editions were printed from the Gutenberg Bible, reinforcing for a while the prevalence of this version.

The Gutenberg Bible was financed, at least in part, by Johann Fust. It was probably this careful businessman who had ensured that all copies were sold before the printing was finished. This we know from Enea Silvio Piccolomini, later Pope Pius II, a papal legate at the imperial diet in Frankfurt am Main in October 1454. There he saw several quires displayed, probably before production was finished. He explained that between approximately 160 and 180 copies were being made. But he was unable to obtain a copy for Cardinal Juan de Carvajal, for all had been sold in advance. Samples had also been sent to the Emperor.

The Gutenberg Bible is also known as the 42-line Bible, although the opening shown here has only 40 lines to the column: some sheets were produced in two different issues, the first issue having only 40 lines. Later these sheets were reset with 42 lines to the column. Probably Gutenberg and his partner wished to increase the print-run without having to buy more paper. The relevant sheets are all of the first issue in our copy, which is splendidly well preserved with fine contemporary manuscript initials. The red heading — the rubric — is here printed, but in later sheets the red printing was abandoned, and the rubrics were left to be filled in by hand — but as a precaution a sheet of instructions was printed for the rubricator.

Provenance: Erhard Nenninger (c.1420-75), mayor of Heilbronn; presented by him to the Carmelites in Heilbronn, not after 1473; in 1633 presented by the city of Heilbronn to Axel Oxenstierna, Swedish plenipotentiary in Germany during the Thirty Years' War; Cardinal E.C. de Loménie de Brienne, before 1791; bought by the Bodleian in 1793, for the sum of £100, one-fifth of the entire budget for book buying for that year.

Literature: F.-X. Laire, *Index librorum ab inventa typographia ad annum 1500* (Sens, 1791), vol. I, 9; H. Hummel, *Katalog der Inkunabeln des Stadtarchivs Heilbronn* (Heilbronn, 1981), 67-68; P. Needham, 'The Paper Supply of the Gutenberg Bible', *The Papers of the Bibliographical Society of America* 79 (1985), 303-374, census no. 22.

Arch. B b.10 (fol. 5r)

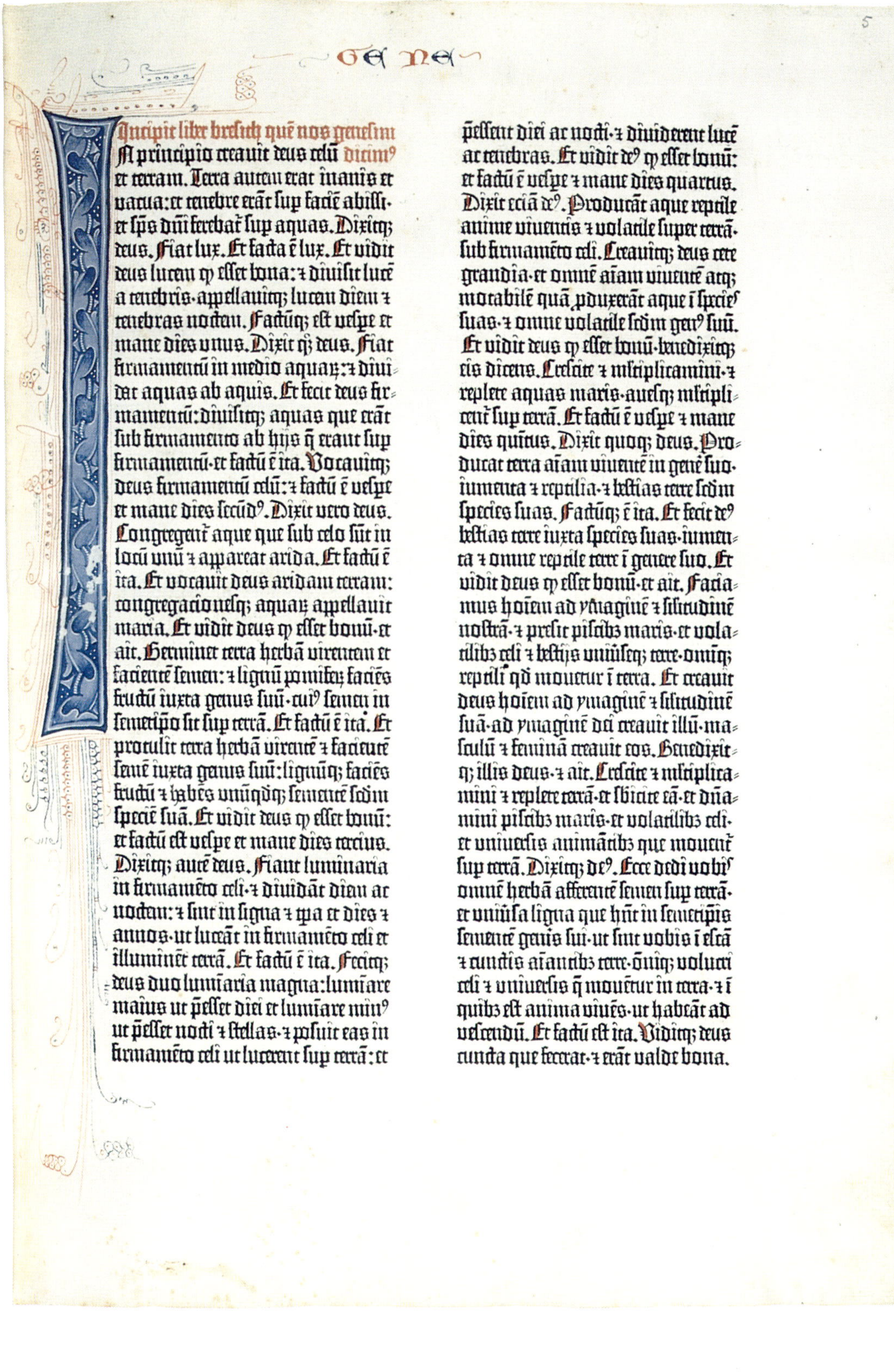

5

Incipit liber bresith quē nos genesim
In principio creauit deus celū dicim⁹
et terram. Terra autem erat inanis et
vacua: et tenebre erāt sup faciē abissi.
et sp̄s dn̄i ferebat̄ sup aquas. Dixitq;
deus. Fiat lux. Et facta ē lux. Et vidit
deus lucem q̄ esset bona: ⁊ diuisit lucē
a tenebris. appellauitq; lucem diem ⁊
tenebras noctem. Factūq; est vespe et
mane dies vnus. Dixit q̄z deus. Fiat
firmamentū in medio aquaꝝ: ⁊ diui-
dat aquas ab aquis. Et fecit deus fir-
mamentū: diuisitq; aquas que erāt
sub firmamento ab hiis q̄ erant sup
firmamentū. et factū ē ita. Vocauitq;
deus firmamentū celū: ⁊ factū ē vespe
et mane dies secūd⁹. Dixit vero deus.
Congregent̄ aque que sub celo sūt in
locū vnū ⁊ appareat arida. Et factū ē
ita. Et vocauit deus aridam terram:
congregacionesq; aquaꝝ appellauit
maria. Et vidit deus q̄ esset bonū. et
ait. Germinet terra herbā virentem et
facientē semen: ⁊ lignū pomiferū faciēs
fructū iuxta genus suū. cui⁹ semen in
semetipo sit sup terrā. Et factū ē ita. Et
protulit terra herbā virentē ⁊ facientē
semē iuxta genus suū: lignūq; faciēs
fructū ⁊ habēs vnūqdq; sementē scd̄m
speciē suā. Et vidit deus q̄ esset bonū:
et factū est vespe et mane dies tercius.
Dixitq; autē deus. Fiant luminaria
in firmamēto celi. ⁊ diuidāt diem ac
noctem: ⁊ sint in signa ⁊ tp̄a et dies ⁊
annos. ut luceāt in firmamēto celi et
illuminēt terrā. Et factū ē ita. Fecitq;
deus duo lumīaria magna: lumīare
maius ut p̄esset diei et lumīare min⁹
ut p̄esset nocti ⁊ stellas. ⁊ posuit eas in
firmamēto celi ut lucerent sup terrā: et
p̄essent diei ac nocti. ⁊ diuiderent lucē
ac tenebras. Et vidit de⁹ q̄ esset bonū:
et factū ē vespe ⁊ mane dies quartus.
Dixit etiā de⁹. Producāt aque reptile
anime viuentis ⁊ volatile super terrā.
sub firmamēto celi. Creauitq; deus cete
grandia. et omnē aīam viuentē atq;
motabilē quā p̄duxerāt aque ī species
suas. ⁊ omne volatile scd̄m gen⁹ suū.
Et vidit deus q̄ esset bonū. benedixitq;
eis dicens. Crescite ⁊ multiplicamini. ⁊
replete aquas maris. auesq; multipli-
centur sup terrā. Et factū ē vespe ⁊ mane
dies quintus. Dixit quoq; deus. Pro-
ducat terra aīam viuentē in genē suo.
iumenta ⁊ reptilia. ⁊ bestias terre scd̄m
species suas. Factūq; ē ita. Et fecit de⁹
bestias terre iuxta species suas. iumen-
ta ⁊ omne reptile terre ī genere suo. Et
vidit deus q̄ esset bonū. et ait. Facia-
mus hoīem ad ymaginē ⁊ similitudinē
nostrā. ⁊ p̄sit piscibꝫ maris. et vola-
tilibꝫ celi ⁊ bestiis vniūseq; terre. omīq;
reptili qd̄ mouetur ī terra. Et creauit
deus hoīem ad ymaginē ⁊ similitudinē
suā. ad ymaginē dei creauit illū. ma-
sculū ⁊ feminā creauit eos. Benedixit-
q; illis deus. ⁊ ait. Crescite ⁊ multiplica-
mini ⁊ replete terrā. et subicite eā. et dn̄a-
mini piscibꝫ maris. et volatilibꝫ celi.
et vniuersis animātibꝫ que mouent̄
sup terrā. Dixitq; de⁹. Ecce dedi vobis
omnē herbā afferentē semen sup terrā.
et vniūsa ligna que hn̄t in semetipis
sementē gen̄is sui. ut sint vobis ī escā
⁊ cunctis aīantibꝫ terre. omīq; volucri
celi ⁊ vniuersis q̄ mouentur in terra. ⁊ ī
quibꝫ est anima viuēs. ut habeāt ad
vescendū. Et factū est ita. Viditq; deus
cuncta que fecerat. ⁊ erāt valde bona.

Monastic Life

17 The Rule of St. Benedict.
England; early 8th century.
i + 77 leaves; 305 x 215 mm.

'The oldest existing copy of a document of primary importance in the making of Europe' (Farmer). St. Benedict (*c*.480–*c*.550) was born at Nursia in Umbria, studied in Rome, and became a hermit at Subiaco, where he was joined by disciples. His rule of monastic life was finished at Monte Cassino, near Naples, where he had moved in *c*.525. Drawing on the earlier rules of St. Basil, St. John Cassian, and others, its austere but humane regime, with communal worship at its heart, was to become the fundamental monastic code in western Europe and the visible link between a multitude of initially autonomous abbeys. Benedict's success stemmed not least from his equal attention to spiritual and to organizational detail.

The diffusion of his Rule in the early Middle Ages was uneven. The monumental formality of this manuscript, which was usually reserved for books of the Bible and indicates a deep veneration for the text, is all the more striking in that it was written at a time when Benedict's Rule had not yet been established as the norm for the religious life in England. Moreover, the existence here of variant readings in the hand of the original scribe suggests the presence in England even at this early date of another manuscript containing a different version of the text. The stately English uncial script was the fruit of the union of the calligraphic traditions of Celtic Northumbria with the Roman uncial of imported manuscripts such as the Laudian Acts (no. 14). Each chapter begins with a vermilion initial letter outlined in black, surrounded by the dots characteristic of Insular decoration.

Provenance: at Worcester Cathedral Priory by the end of the 11th century, and still in c.1622–3; bought by the Bodleian through the London bookseller Robert Scot, 1671, from the library of Christopher, first Baron Hatton.

Literature: SC 4118; CLA ii, no. 240; P & A iii, no. 1; D.H. Farmer, *The Rule of St. Benedict. Oxford, Bodleian Library, Hatton 48* (Early English Manuscripts in Facsimile 15: Copenhagen, 1968).

 MS. Hatton 48 (fol. 29r)

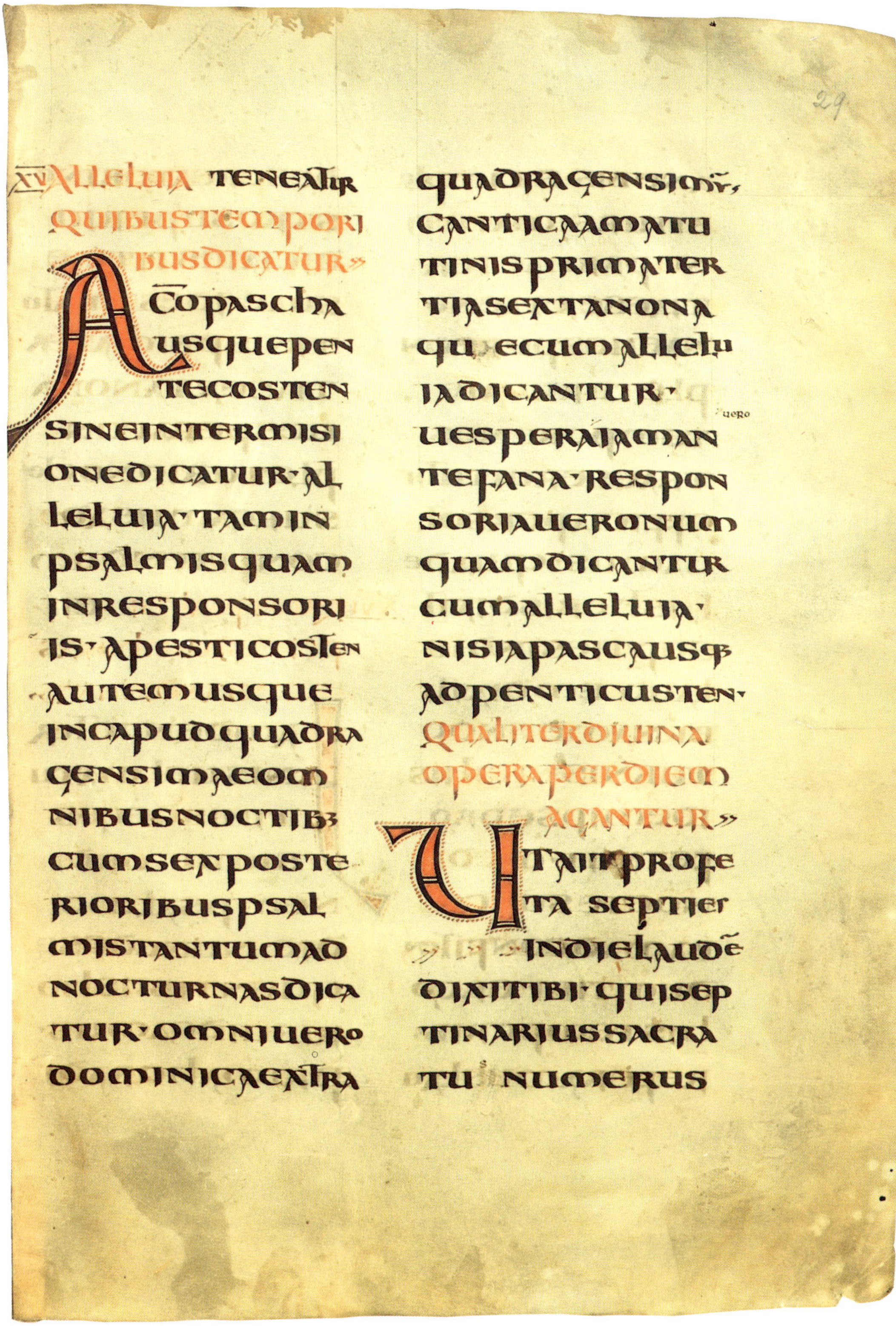

XV ALLELUIA TENEATUR
QUIBUS TEMPORI
BUS DICATUR
A Co PASCHA
USQUE PEN
TECOSTEN
SINE INTERMISI
ONE DICATUR AL
LELUIA TAM IN
PSALMIS QUAM
IN RESPONSORI
IS A PESTICOSTEN
AUTEM USQUE
IN CAPUD QUADRA
GENSIMAE OM
NIBUS NOCTIB;
CUM SEX POSTE
RIORIBUS PSAL
MIS TANTUM AD
NOCTURNAS DICA
TUR OMNI UERO
DOMINICA EXTRA
QUADRAGENSIMO
CANTICA A MATU
TINIS PRIMA TER
TIA SEXTA NONA
QU ECUM ALLELU
IA DICANTUR
UESPERA IAM AN (uero)
TEFANA RESPON
SORIA UERO NUM
QUAM DICANTUR
CUM ALLELUIA
NISI A PASCA USQ;
AD PENTICUSTEN
QUALITER DIUINA
OPERA PER DIEM
AGANTUR
UT AIT PROFE
TA SEPTIES
IN DIE LAUDE
DIXI TIBI QUI SEP
TINARIUS SACRA
TU NUMERUS

The Classics and Christendom

Monastic Production of Printed Books

18 St. Augustine, *De civitate Dei.*
[Subiaco: Conrad Sweynheym and Arnold Pannartz] 1467, 2°.
271 leaves; 315 x 215 mm.

Provenance: Subiaco, Benedictine convent, St. Scholastica; probably the copy given by Subiaco to Pius VI in 1776; Louis César de la Baume le Blanc, Duc de La Vallière (1708-80); Vallière sale, part 1 (Paris, 1783), no. 448; Pierre-Antoine Bolongaro-Crevenna (1735-92); Crevenna sale (1789), part 1, no. 479; purchased by the Bodleian in 1790 for £19.5.0.

Literature: C. Frova, M. Miglio, 'Dal MS Sublacense XLII all'*editio princeps* del "De civitate Dei" di Sant' Agostino (Hain 2046)', in *Scrittura biblioteche e stampa a Roma nel quattrocento, Aspetti e problemi, Atti del seminario 1-2 Giugno 1979*, eds. C. Bianca, P. Farenga *et al.* (Vatican 1980), 245-73; L. Hellinga, 'The Codex in the Fifteenth Century: Manuscript and Print', in *A Potencie of Life*, ed. N. Barker (London, 1993), 63-88, here pp. 71-74; G. P. Carosi, *Badia di Subiaco* (Subiaco, 1970), 69, on the gift to Pius VI.

Printing spread relatively slowly for the first few years. But with the sack of Mainz in October 1462 Sweynheym and Pannartz departed. They had probably been employees of Johann Fust and Peter Schoeffer who had continued Johann Gutenberg's printing shop (see no. 16). Settling in the monastery of Subiaco, in the hills of Lazio, Sweynheym and Pannartz became the first printers in Italy: migrant craftsmen, in this case possibly refugees, soon spread the art of printing throughout most of Europe. Their mobility was possible largely because, no matter where in Europe, their readers used the same language. That two German printers should have settled in Subiaco illustrates the continuity between late medieval book production and early printing, as well as the importance of religious orders as international institutions, facilitating cultural contacts across Europe. Most printing in the 15th century was performed in secular printing houses but it was often sponsored by ecclesiastical bodies. Continuity with manuscript production is here further emphasized by the hand-painted initials. Other important features of the page layout — running headings and chapter headings — were also added by hand in red ink. It has recently been discovered that our copy belonged to the convent of Subiaco itself. A deleted ownership inscription dating from the 17th century is found at the bottom of the page shown here.

Augustine's *City of God* was a central link between the ancient pagan world and the Christian Middle Ages. Written following the sack of Rome by the Goths in 410, it was a religious reassessment of the secular power of the ancient world, rejecting the moral values which had been perceived as the basis for the Roman Empire. It was among the most influential texts for medieval political and religious thought and remained so for much of the early modern period as well.

 Auct. 7Q 2.19 (fol. 13r)

INTEREA cũ Roma gothorũ irruptione agentium sub Rege Alarico atq; ĩpetu magnę cladis euersa est: eius euersionem deorũ falsorũ multorũq; cultores quos usitato noĩe paganos uocamus: in christianã religionem referre conantes: solito acerbius & amarius deũ uerũ blasfemare cęperũt. Unde ego exardescens zelo domus dei: aduersus eorum blasfemias uel errores: libros de ciuitate dei scribere istitui. Quod opus per aliquot annos me tenuit. eo ꝙ alia multa intercurrebãt quę differri nõ oporteret: et me prius ad soluendum occupabant. Hoc aũt de ciuitate dei grãde opus tandem .xxii. libris est terminatum. quorum quinq; primi eos refellunt q res humanas ita prosperari uolũt: ut ad hoc multorũ deorũ cultũ quos pagani colere consueuerunt: necessariũ esse arbitrẽtur. et quia ꝓhibentur: mala ista exoriri atq; abũdare contẽdunt. Sequẽtes aũt quinq;: aduersus eos loquũtur qui fatentur hęc mala nec defuisse unquam nec defutura mortalib9: & ea nunc magna: nunc pua: locis: temporibus: psonisq; uariari. Sed deorũ multorũ cultũ quo eis sacrificatur: propter uitam post mortem futuram esse utilem disputant. His ergo .x. libris duę istę uanę opiniones christianę religioni aduersarię refelluntur. Sed ne quisq̃ nos aliena tantum redarguisse: non aũt nr̃a asseruisse reprehẽderet: id agit ps altera operis huius. quę .xii. libris continetur. Quanq̃ ubi opus est: & in priorib9 .x. quę nr̃a sũt asseramus: et in .xii. posteriorib9 redarguamus aduersa. Duodecim ergo librorũ sequentiũ primi quatuor cõtinẽt exortum duarũ ciuitatum. quarũ ẽ una dei altera huius mũdi. Secũdi quatuor excursũ earũ seu procursum. Tertii uero qui et postremi: debitos fines. Ita omnes .xxii. libri cũ sint de utraq; ciuitate conscripti: titulũ tamen a meliore acceperũt. ut de ciuitate dei potius uocarentur. In quorũ decimo libro nõ debuit ꝓ miraculo poni: in Abrahę sacrificio flammã cęlitus factam iter diuisas uictimas cucurrisse. qm̃ hoc illi in uisione mostratũ est. In .xii. libro quod dictum ẽ de Samuele nõ erat de filiis Aaron: dicẽdum potius ẽ fuit, nõ erat filius sacerdotis. Filios quippe sacerdotum defunctis sacerdotibus succedere magis legictimi moris fuit. Nam in filiis Aaron repit̃ pr̃ Samuelis. sed sacerdos nõ fuit. nec ita in filiis ut eũ ipse genuerit Aaron: sed sicut omẽs illius ppli dicũtur filii israel.

GLoriosissimã ciuitatem dei siue in hoc tẽporũ cursu cũ inter impios pegrinat̃ ex fide uiuens: siue in illa stabilitate sedis ęternę quam nũc expectat per patientiam: quoadusq; iustitia cõuertatur in iudicium: deinceps adeptura per excellentiã uictoria ultima et pace pfc̃ta: hoc ope ad te instituto & mea ꝓmissione debito: defendere aduersus eos q conditori eius deos suos preferũt fili carissime Marcelline suscepi. magnum opus et arduum: sed deus adiutor noster est. Nam scio qbus uiribus opus sit: ut psuadeat̃ supbis quanta sit uirtus humilitatis. qua fit ut omnia terrena cacumina temporali mobilitate nutantia: nõ hũano usurpata fastu: sed diuina gratia donata celsitudo transcendat. Rex. n. & cõditor ciuitatis

Printing for Bishops

19 *Missale herbipolense.*
[Würzburg:] J. Reyser, 1481, 2°. 376 leaves; 400 x 270 mm.

During the 1460s and 1470s nearly all missals produced were the *Missale Romanum*. This was not adapted to any specific local use, but could be sold to any institution. In the 1480s a trend appeared to print missals according to local uses. This book is an early example, again illustrating how printing was not exclusively a capitalist enterprise, but frequently dependent on patronage (see no. 18). Reyser, the printer, worked for Rudolph von Scherenberg, the prince-bishop of Würzburg, and produced books for use in his diocese.

In his prefatory letter in the missal, the prince-bishop explains that he had the missal printed because the manuscripts which were in use in his diocese were often in a bad state of preservation, and their texts at variance with one another. The printed missal represented a revised, uniform version for the entire diocese. Again we see printing as a tool in the creation of uniformity, this time on a local level. The attempt was reinforced by the bishop's request of all the clerics in his diocese to buy Reyser's work — the price had been fixed at four Rhenish guilders — and as further inducement he granted forty days of indulgence to all who were involved in the production of the book, or who bought it, or who read or heard mass from it. That is probably why there were six editions of it in Reyser's lifetime. In 1481 our copy was bought, rubricated, illuminated and bound for 18 guilders at the expense of Johannes Keusch, the vicar of the altar of St. Bartholomew in the cathedral in Würzburg. This is a copy printed on parchment, which was more expensive than paper, so it is likely that Keusch had to pay more than the stipulated 4 guilders for the printed sheets.

The use of the book in the liturgy of public worship is reflected in its bulk and in the size of the typeface employed, especially here in the canon of the mass, the section of the missal which was in daily use. While the typeface was indisputably designed to be monumental, it also served the practical purpose of making the text easy to read while it was standing on its lectern.

Provenance: Johannes Keusch, Würzburg, 1481; donated by him to the altar of St. Bartholomew in 1486; signed by other vicars between 1565 and 1606; probably alienated during the Swedish sack of Würzburg in 1631; acquired by William Laud (1573–1645), Archbishop of Canterbury, who donated it to the University in 1636.

Auct. 1Q 1.7 (fol. 149r)

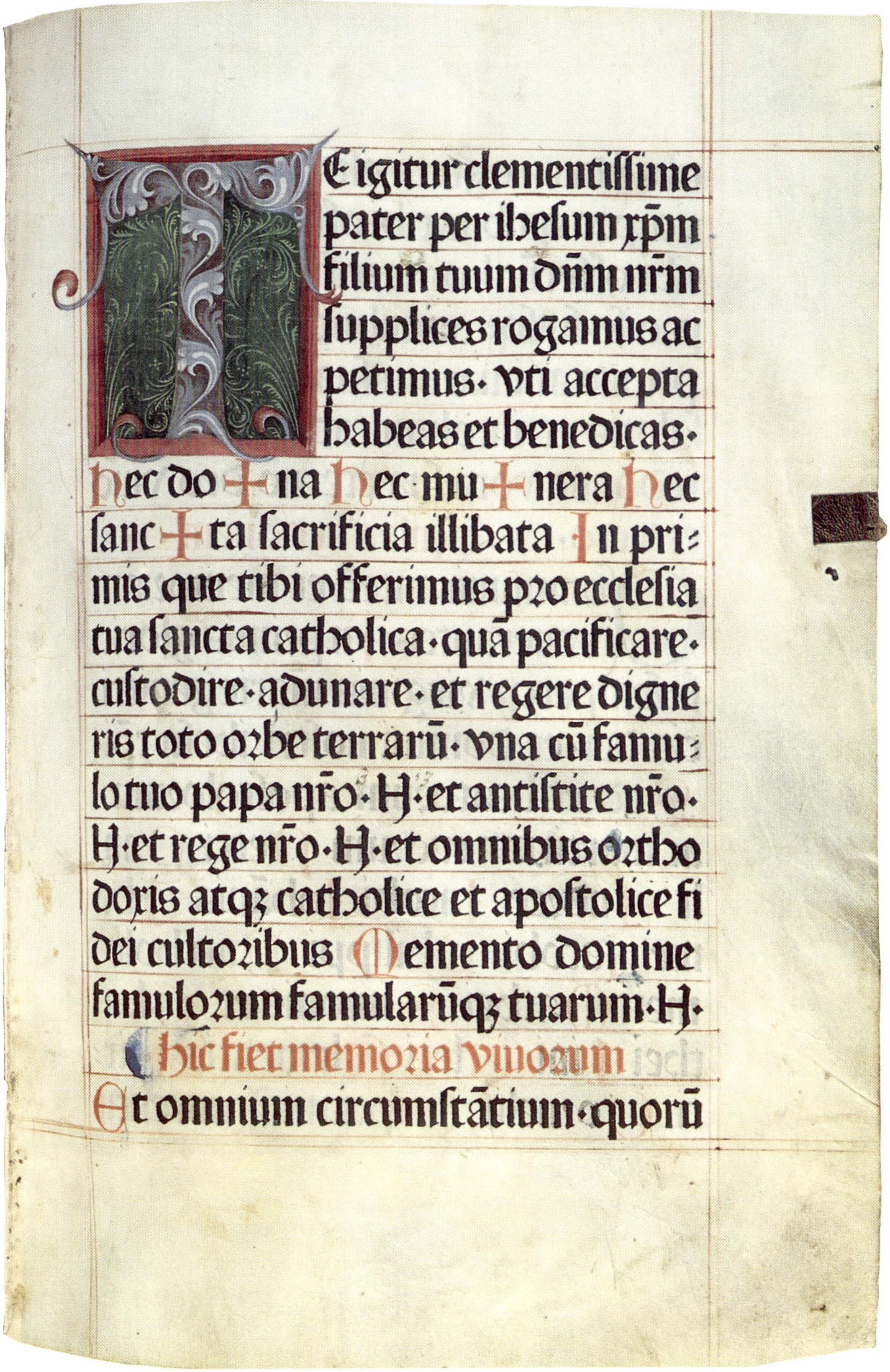

Te igitur clementissime
pater per ihesum xp̄m
filium tuum dn̄m nr̄m
supplices rogamus ac
petimus. uti accepta
habeas et benedicas.
Hec do + na Hec mu + nera Hec
sanc + ta sacrificia illibata In pri-
mis que tibi offerimus pro ecclesia
tua sancta catholica. quā pacificare.
custodire. adunare. et regere digne
ris toto orbe terrarū. una cū famu-
lo tuo papa nr̄o. N. et antistite nr̄o.
N. et rege nr̄o. N. et omnibus ortho
doxis atqz catholice et apostolice fi
dei cultoribus Memento domine
famulorum famularūqz tuarum. N.
Hic fiet memoria vivorum
Et omnium circumstātium. quorū

The Classics and Christendom

Private Devotion

20 Book of Hours According to the Use of Rome.
[Augsburg:] Johann Schönsperger, 1513, 2°. 157 leaves; 245 x 165 mm.

Books of Hours were for private devotional purposes, providing a structure within which individual religious acts could be performed, at home or in a private chapel. The private nature of this Book of Hours is emphasised by the history of its production. It was commissioned by Maximilian I (1459-1519), who asked for ten copies to be printed, all on parchment; eight are known to survive, of which three are in Oxford, two in the Bodleian and one in Keble College. No calendar of saints was printed for the Book of Hours: all the surviving copies are evidence of a project never completed.

A copy decorated in part by Albrecht Dürer convinced Erwin Panofsky that the ten copies were proof copies only. He argued that Dürer's drawings were meant as drafts for woodcuts which were to be reproduced in a final edition. This would have been an unusual procedure, and it seems implausible that proofs would be printed on parchment, which was more expensive than paper. However, many of the Emperor's plans involved experimenting with unusual techniques, and he undoubtedly aimed at an unusual production. Early printers had produced books which looked very much like manuscripts: that was what books had always looked like (see nos 12, 13, 16, 18 and 19). This book, however, was a conscious attempt to create a printed book which looked like an old manuscript. In our copy this impression is enhanced by the hand-painted decoration, done in a Flemish style, but the typeface itself also contributes to this end. Designed for this book specifically, possibly by Vincenz Roder in Maximilian's Viennese chancellery, the size of the typeface relative to the page recalls the proportions of much earlier Books of Hours. The extravagant imitations of penflourishes are perhaps the most remarkable feature. They and the small detached flourishes floating above some letters are believed to be the work of the Fleming Just de Negher. Working in Schönsperger's workshop, he was known also for his skills in printing in several colours. Craftsmen with a remarkable range of skills were gathered in the southern German cities, encouraged and supported by frequent and demanding Imperial commissions (see also no. 55).

Provenance: bequeathed to the Bodleian by Francis Douce (1757-1834).

Literature: *Douce Legacy* no. 130; E. Panofsky, *Albrecht Dürer* (Princeton, 1943); E. Cockx-Indestege, 'Das"Gepeet puechl extraordinarij" oder Das Stundenbuch des Kaisers Maximilian I.', in *Ars impressoria. Entstehung und Entwicklung des Buchdrucks. Eine internationale Festgabe für Severin Corsten zum 65. Geburtstag*, eds. H. Limburg *et al.* (Munich 1986), 231-50, no. 8; H. Horninger, 'Zwei neue exemplare des "Maximilian-Gebetbuches" ', *Gutenberg-Jahrbuch* (1976), 207-212.

Douce FF 59 (pp. 68-69)

68.
tre et spiritusancto glorie viuit
et regnat in secula seculorum.
Amen.
Hore intemerate virginis Ma
rie secundum vsum Romane
curie. Ad matutinas.
Domine labia mea ape
ries. Et os meum an
nunctiabit laudem tuã. De
us in adiutorium meum intẽ
de. Domine ad adiuuãdum
me festina. Gloria patri et fi
lio: et spiritusãctõ. Sicut erat
69.
in principio et nunc et semper:
et in secula seculorum Amen.
Alleluia. Et dr. Alleluia a pa
scha vsq ad septuagesimam:
et a septuagesima vsq ad pa
scha dicitur. Laus tibi domi
ne: rex eterne glorie. Inuitato
rium. Aue maria gratia ple
na. Dominus tecũ. Aue ma
ria. Psalmus.
Venite exultemus domi
no: iubilemus deo salu
tari nostro: preoccupemus fa
ciem eius in confessione: et in

The Classics and Christendom

Devotional Pictures for Collectors

21 *Passio domini nostri Jesu ex Hieronymo Padovano, Domenico Mancino, et Baptista Mantuano per fratrem Chelidonium* [i.e. Benedictus Schwalbe] *collecta, cum figuris Alberti Dureri Norici pictoris.*
Nürnberg: [H. Hölzel for] A. Dürer, 1511, 2°. 12 leaves; 485 x 325 mm.

In 1511 Albrecht Dürer published three large books: the Life of the Virgin, The Apocalypse of St. John and the 'Large Passion'. All three are contained in this volume. Most of the woodcuts had been published before: The Bearing of the Cross shown here was cut in 1498-99 (Panofsky no. 230). Panofsky found that the plates of, for instance, the so-called 'Engraved Passion' were collectors' items, whereas these books, having a text facing each illustration, were intended for devotion. This is difficult to understand: these books were never cheap and must also have been 'collectors' items'. At the same time the illustrations were undoubtedly meant to assist private devotional activity, or to display semi-publicly the private devotion of the owner. The contemporary Nürnberg binding on our copy shows traces of having been decorated in gold and silver, a very rare procedure in Germany in this period, and is further evidence that these books were considered luxury items.

Already around 1500 Dürer was being called the modern Apelles: his greatness equalled that of the greatest painter of antiquity. This description of Dürer gained Europe-wide currency after 1528 when Erasmus's eulogy of him was included in his much-read book on Latin and Greek pronunciation. In Pliny's *Historia naturalis* artists were discussed in connection with the stones or minerals which they used. Erasmus drew heavily on Pliny's description of Apelles (*Historia naturalis* xxxv. 96), but Dürer's skills exceeded his: without the use of colour he expressed shade, radiance, projections and depressions. Developing Pliny's theme that Apelles painted things which could not be painted, such as lightning, Erasmus said that Dürer painted the mind of man and almost his voice. Erasmus firmly established the heroic stature of Dürer, borrowing such rhetorical themes from Pliny. Philip Melanchthon struck a tone perhaps more sympathetic to the modern ear, writing that Dürer had told him how, as a young man, he had found colours irresistible, but that he had come to regard simplicity as the greatest of arts: he was rather embarrassed when confronted with the paintings of his younger years.

Provenance: contemporary Nürnberg binding: see K. Haebler, *Rollen- und Plattenstempel des 16. Jahrhunderts*, vol. 2 (Leipzig, 1929), 108, rolls 4 and 6, used on records from 1514-18 in the Nürnberg Stadtarchiv; in the library of the Bavarian noble family Reisach by 1800; bequeathed to the Bodleian by Francis Douce (1757-1834).

Literature: Douce Legacy no. 138; E. Panofsky, Albrecht Dürer (Princeton, 1943), no. 231; J. Meder, *Dürer-Katalog. Ein Handbuch über Dürers Stiche, Radierungen, Holzschnitte, deren Zustände, Ausgaben und Wasserzeichen* (Vienna, 1932), no. 120; J. Białostocki, *Dürer and his Critics 1500-1971* (Baden-Baden, 1986).

Douce D subt. 41(2) (fol. 7r)

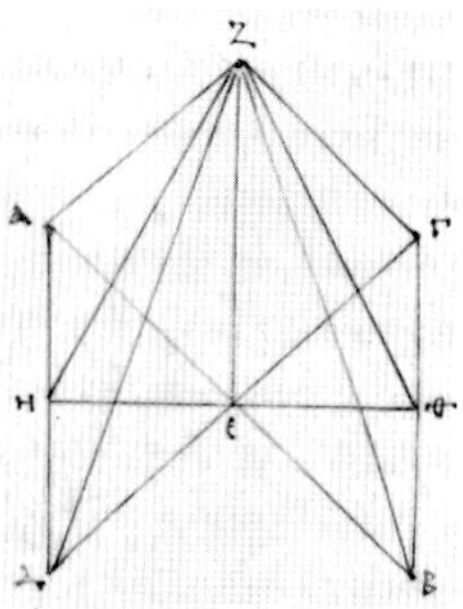

International Languages - International Learning

The Latin language established a linguistic community in Europe, effectively defining a social group. Numerically a relatively small part of the European population, the men — and to some extent women — who knew Latin were of a disproportionate importance in political, cultural and religious life. A person with no Latin would find access to a number of important fields very difficult indeed. Language was a means of social differentiation as well as of communication.

The language of the Church was also the language of the universities, where the three professional faculties prepared men for careers in law, medicine and theology. The University of Bologna was the international centre for the study of law (no. 22). From the 12th century Roman Law gradually gained in importance; while it never entirely replaced local customary or statutory law, it did provide an academic intellectual framework within which legal studies were pursued, even in England where Henry VIII founded chairs in Roman Law at both Oxford and Cambridge. Thus an internationally compatible set of legal concepts was established. The universities also taught canon law, a legal system competing and interlocking with that of civil law. Through the bureaucracy of the Church, canon law influenced the daily life of medieval Europe more deeply than any other of the disciplines taught at universities (no. 23).

The academic study of law depended on the interpretation of texts. The correct understanding of the legal texts could not be achieved without a thorough knowledge of Latin. A similar attitude was evident also in the study of medicine: the correct understanding of the authoritative texts was essential for creating a technical language upon which all could agree. In medicine it could have disastrous consequences if a property was ascribed to a plant, but the plant incorrectly named. With the process of creating a common Latin and Greek nomenclature, the foundations were also laid for creating compatible vernacular European nomenclatures: illustrations played an important role as an aid to correct identification. Conrad Gesner's works on natural history are important for this development (no. 25). In some senses this aspect of Gesner's activity continued a tradition which originated in the monastic world. The medieval herbal from Bury St. Edmunds (no. 24) was also a medical text with a classical background: a Latinized Greek work glossed with vernacular names.

In the Eastern Empire, the connection back to the ancient world was much more continuous, and Greek texts dealing with technical and scientific matters, unavailable in the West, were produced and read there (no. 28). From the 12th century onwards a great number of Greek works were translated into Latin, most often from Arabic or Hebrew versions (no. 49): Spanish Jews and Muslims were particularly important in this process. The early 15th century saw an increased interest in Greek in the West, and now many works were directly translated, for instance Ptolemy's *Cosmography* (no. 3). Increasingly, towards the end of the 15th century, production began of Greek books in Greek, often aided by Greeks resident in the West: Aldus Manutius's Aristotle in Greek (no. 29) relied in part on the work of Greeks, and the printing of Simplicius's Commentary on Aristotle (no. 31) was both financed and produced by Greeks.

Hebrew was also a learned international language in Europe, despite the obstacles imposed by an often hostile environment on the establishment of stable institutions in which its study could be promoted. The legal commentary (no. 32) printed in Constantinople by a Spaniard, using a typeface produced in Italy, is evidence of a concept of Europe defined as a religious, not as a geographical, entity — Europeans defined themselves by segregating, persecuting or expelling those who did not belong.

Law

22 Azo, *Summa* on the *Codex* and *Institutes*.
Bologna; late 13th century.
iii + 351 leaves; 435 x 270 mm.

In 13th-century Europe, the University of Bologna was to legal studies what the University of Paris was to Biblical studies and theology: the international centre. Both the fundamental categories of academic law were taught: civil (or secular) law, and canon (or ecclesiastical) law. Canon law consisted of the decisions of Church councils, and collections of papal and episcopal letters dealing with specific subjects, known as Decretals. The basis of civil law was the code assembled for the Emperor Justinian (pictured here) in the 6th century AD, consisting of extracts from ancient Roman law with additions from Justinian's own time.

The rediscovery of the corpus of civil law at Bologna was not primarily a practical answer to the needs of society: it was an academic endeavour in which commentators such as Azo (*c.*1150-*c.*1230), like their colleagues in other disciplines such as philosophy and natural science, attempted to assimilate the learning of Antiquity. Gradually, however, Roman law did penetrate the law courts of Europe (except in England, where Common Law continued to hold sway). Justinianic law belonged to Rome's imperial age, and provided a picture of a centralized state directed by a prince, with qualified judges and officials applying universal norms of justice; such a model proved attractive to rulers attempting to transform loose conglomerates, based on the fragmented authority of feudal customary law, into unified states.

The need of the new universities for textbooks brought about a new medieval book trade, in which booksellers or stationers mediated between professional scribes and illuminators and their customers. This de-luxe law book, elaborately illuminated, must still have been produced within the University sphere, since it contains marginal notes marking the ends of the 'peciae', or sections of text, which the stationers hired out to scribes for copying a few leaves at a time.

Provenance: 14th-century monogram, 'S.I.' or 'I.S.', fol. 2r and elsewhere; sold by the Discalced Augustinians of Lyons to Thomas Coke, later first Earl of Leicester, probably in 1715-16; Holkham Hall MS. 206; accepted by HM Treasury from the executors of the fifth Earl in part satisfaction of Capital Transfer Tax, and allocated to the Bodleian, 1981.

Literature: W.O. Hassall, *The Holkham Library. Illuminations and Illustrations in the Manuscript Library of the Earl of Leicester* (Roxburghe Club 218: Oxford, 1970), 20-21, pls. 61- 9; A.C. de la Mare, 'Further Manuscripts from Holkham Hall', *BLR* 10 (1978-82), 327-38, pp. 330-33; 'Further Italian Illuminated Manuscripts', no. 5.

MS. Holkham misc. 47 (fol. 254r)

International Learning

The Availability of Law Books

23 Book-hawker's advertisement.
[Nürnberg: F. Creussner, *c.*1477]. Single sheet; 290 x 205 mm.

This printed single sheet is an advertisement for an itinerant bookseller, giving a list of the books which he sold and telling customers to go to a locality, the name of which has been left blank by the printer to be filled in as appropriate for each town or city to which the bookseller came. The thirty-one books on the list were printed in Nürnberg, Augsburg, Strasbourg and Basel and they are all in Latin, but none of them are Latin classics. Most of the books offered for sale are on canon law and meant for men in the service of the church. Canon law was relevant to many areas of human activity which we would not now regard as part of ecclesiastical life — for instance legal disputes over contracts which involved oaths; and, for the many among the literate who could be considered clerics, it was an alternative legal system to civil law. When taking confession priests were confronted with legal problems which they needed to solve: manuals of confession contain much material which is legal advice. An instrument of the transnational Church, canon law in Latin made western Europe a legal union.

Our copy carries the inscription 'Ad sanctam Mariam Magdalenam', probably the name of an inn — 'The Magdalen Arms' — where the bookseller would be offering his merchandise. The inscription is on the back of the leaf, which suggests that this may be a hand bill, not a poster. This little sheet gives an indication of the geographical penetration of canon law, even in smaller places with no resident book-seller. Few texts other than law achieved such wide distribution: in the 16th century the complaint was heard that only law books could be had in small towns where books were only available from travelling dealers.

Provenance: acquired in 1951 from the Oxford bookseller Albi Rosenthal by Albert Ehrman (1890-1969); given to the Bodleian by John Ehrman in 1978.

Literature: the Bodleian copy is reproduced in H. G. Pollard, A. Ehrman, *The Distribution of Books by Catalogue* (Cambridge, 1965), frontispiece.

Volentes emere libros infrascriptos
veniant ad locum subscriptum.

Postillam fratris nicolai de lira super vtrumqꝫ testamentum
cum expositionibus omnium prologorum.
Speculum naturale vincencij.
Speculum hystoriale vincencij.
Joannem ianuensem in catholicon
Bibliam nouum et vetus continens testamentū
Pantheologiam. Textum sententiarum.
Summam pysani. Summam astexam.
Vocabularium salomonis.

Opus preclarum pene inuisum Quod elucidariꝰ scripturarum
intitulatᷣ | declarans rarissimos terminos veteris nouiqꝫ testa
mēti | necnō t'minoꝝ grecoꝝ et ebraycoꝝ int'ptacōs elucidans
Rationale diuinorum officiorum.
Continuum beati thome de aquino.
Lombarticam hystoriam cū legendis quibusdā compressis.
Sophilogium. Gregorium in registro.
Vitam b iesu.
Sermones ruberti de licio per aduentum.
Sermones alberti de tempore et de sanctis.
Postillam super euangelia et epistolas.
Decretum graciani
Decretales.
Sextum decretalium.
Clementinas.
Institutiones.
Codicem Justiniani imperatoris.
Repertorium petri brixiensis.
Repertorium caldrini.
Questiones mercuriales ioannis andree

Tractatus poptiꝰ docēs modū studēdi et legendi iura cū ab
breuiaturis suis | et determinans de qua materia in decreto in
quibussuis distinctionibus: causis et questionibus tractatur:
ꝙ inibi querenda citissime inueniantur | continens et metra su-
per eisdem distinctionibus et causis decreti | atqꝫ versus super
rubricam quinqꝫ libroꝝ decretalium. Necnon oēs titulos iam
dictorum librorum decretalium | et omnium librorum iuris ci-
uilis ſm ordinem alphabeti positos.
Arbores consanguinitatis. affi. nec nō spūalis cognationis.

International Learning

Medicine

24 Herbal (with 'Sextus Placitus', *De virtutibus bestiarum in arte medicinae*).
Bury St. Edmunds; late 11th or early 12th century.
vii + 101 leaves; 245 x 180 mm.

The medieval herbal might be defined as natural history being put to work in the service of medicine. This example consists of two of the most popular texts, both of which were associated with classical authors. The pseudo-Apuleius, attributed to the Platonic philosopher of the Antonine period, was probably adapted from a Greek original in the 4th or 5th century AD. The pseudo-Dioscorides was named after the physician of the 1st century AD, whose *De materia medica* was translated from Greek into Latin in the 6th century. A typical entry here gives the Greek name of the herb, a list of synonyms and names in other languages, a short note on the habitat and character of the plant, an enumeration of its virtues (centred on the diseases it can cure), and some recipes. Illustrations were an integral part of such works: here the plants have clearly been drawn first, and the texts subsequently written around them. The accompanying treatise on the medicinal qualities of animals was a natural complement to the herbal, and is also illustrated.

The practical usefulness of such works is disputed. The herbals are arranged by remedy, not condition, though an added index goes some way towards overcoming this here. The major problem was identification and nomenclature: the presence of English plant names, some nearly contemporary with the Latin text, others in later hands, suggests a continuing need to relate the language of the textbook to that of the garden. On the page reproduced, 'herba erusci' is glossed as 'brimbel'. Whereas the tradition of illustrated herbals from the 9th century onwards mostly involved the copying of conventionalized pictures - a necessity for a northern European artist copying a plant encountered only in the Mediterranean - in the case of the bramble, there is clearly an element of the observation of nature. The monk Walafrid Strabo (*c.*808-49) wrote that his knowledge of plants and gardening had been derived from three sources: common knowledge, ancient books, and hard work.

Provenance: given by Sir Thomas Knyvett (d.1594) to Augustine Styward; given to the Bodleian by Edward Tyson in 1706.

Literature: SC 27609; R.T. Gunther, *The Herbal of Apuleius Barbarus from the Early Twelfth-Century Manuscript Formerly in the Abbey of Bury St. Edmunds (MS. Bodley 130)* (Roxburghe Club 167: Oxford, 1925); C. Singer, 'The Herbal in Antiquity and its Transmission to Later Ages', *Journal of Hellenic Studies* 47 (1927), 1-52; P & A iii, no. 53; C.M. Kauffmann, *Romanesque Manuscripts 1066-1190* (A Survey of Manuscripts Illuminated in the British Isles 3: London, 1975), no. 11.

 MS. Bodl. 130 (fol. 26r)

.i. brimbel.

26

Grecis dr. Batosidea.
Alii Cinosbatos.
Prophete Simrophu.
Alii Ematitanos.
Alii Emaideos.
Itali Sinix.
Romani Rubum uocant.
Alii Mora siluatica.

.LXXXVIII.

Nascitur in campis et in sepibus. Ad aurium dolorem. Herbe erusci qui masculus est tepefactus et stillatus aurium pressus in auriculis dolore liberat. et psanare dicimus.

Herba erusci qui mas .IIII. et mirte qui mas idē .VIIII. mali granati sicci cortices teres. decoquantur inse. et catesinas impingue. et cum refrigidauerit fomentabis tibi sessum. hoc pericilum faciens miri fice stringet et sanat. Ad profluuium mulieris. Herbas rusci qui mas teneras ter septenas decoques in aqua usque ad tertias et triduo ieiuno potui dabis ita. ut coicidit nouies potionem. Ad cardiacos. Herba erusci folia per se trita imponuntur et mamille sinistre dolorem tollit. Ad usus gingebarum et dolorum uitia. Herbe erusci cauliset teneros in uino decoquis et ipsum uinum more continebis sume facit. Ad uue remedium. Herbe erusci folia arefiant in ui bri tere in clario facto. resilit in presente nero. Ad uulnera recentia. Herbe erusci flos aut maros sine collecti ones apiculo sanat. Ad edolomata. Herba rubi in uino decocta ad tertias coq: in uino fouebis edolomata et omnia uitia sedat. Nom serpentis sipedon.

Languages of Science

25 Conrad Gesner, *Historia animalium liber iiii qui est de piscium et aquatilium animantium natura.*
Zürich: Christoph Froschauer, 1558, 2°. 1317 leaves; 380 x 230 mm.

Conrad Gesner (1516-65) was a crucial figure in the scientific community of 16th-century Europe. He aimed to publish a complete encyclopedia of the natural world, to replace both the theoretical framework provided by Aristotle's *Physics* and Pliny's *Historia naturalis* (see no.13). Situated centrally in Zürich, he was in touch with scholars and scientists from all over Europe, who, on their frequent visits and in their correspondence with him, reported natural phenomena, and presented specimens of rare and curious plants, animals and minerals. Many of his correspondents were medical men: the connection between medicine and natural history remained strong (see no. 24). Unlike many, Gesner was careful to acknowledge the contributions of other scholars, thus securing their future cooperation. The caption to the illustration shown here indicates that he got his specimen of this fish from Venice, but that he thought that it must have been dried. Therefore he relied on a French colleague for information on its true colours. This must also indicate that the hand-colouring of the plates was done under Gesner's supervision. The illustration is of the fish which in Latin was called the 'rana piscatrix', the 'fishing frog'. Gesner recorded a number of German names but, confronted with a variety of vernacular possibilities, he ended by creating one himself. The English name which he gave, 'tode fish', 'toad fish', is a translation of the first part of the Latin. Today a more common English name is 'the angler', a translation of the second part of the Latin name. The French suggested by Gesner is also based on the Latin name. Here we see the standardisation of vernacular names for natural phenomena in the making. Gesner discussed in his preface the procedure for harmonising vernaculars. His chief informants on English nomenclature were two Marian exiles, John Parkhurst (1522?-75) and William Turner (d. 1568). Accompanying these works, Gesner published tables relating English, French, German, Italian and Spanish vernacular names for natural phenomena to the established Latin and Greek terminology. His works on language and on natural history were closely related. The dichotomy which some modern scholars have seen between his philological and his scientific interests reflect our divisions, not those of 16th-century Europe.

Provenance: a 16th-century Parisian institution; 'Debaillon' [17th century?]; bequeathed to the Bodleian by Francis Douce (1757-1834).

Douce G subt. 54
(pp. 960-961)

Icon hæc est Ranæ piscatricis, qualem Venetijs depictam olim ab amico accepi. conijcio autem ad piscem aridum factam esse. Rondeletij enim pictura quin legitima sit, non dubito.

B.

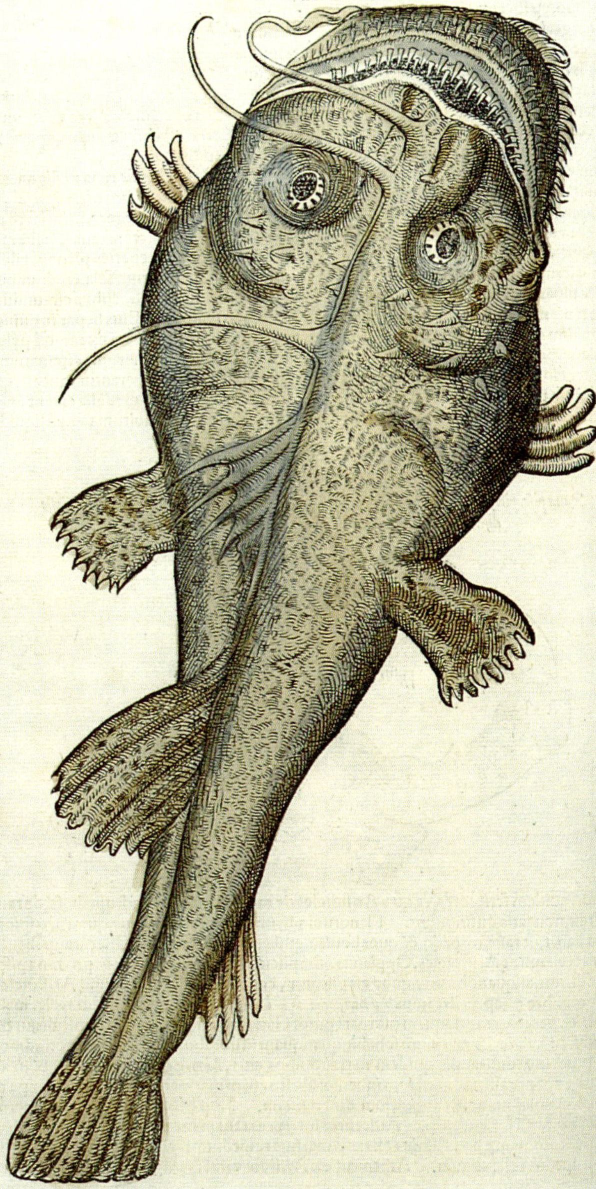

Βάτραχ

International Learning

Launching a Discovery

26 William Harvey, *Exercitatio anatomica de motu cordis et sanguinis in animalibus.* Frankfurt am Main: William Fitzer, 1628, 4°. 108 pp; 180 x 140 mm.

'If ever a book of outstanding importance crept quietly into the world it surely was Harvey's Exercitatio anatomica' (Keynes). It was an unspectacular little book which carried the revolutionary discovery of Harvey (1578-1657) on the function of the heart and the circulation of the blood. Despite its scruffy appearance, the book was advertised for sale at the next Frankfurt fair after its publication, and the work gained the diffusion which Harvey had wished to obtain by publishing abroad. He had done so at the recommendation of Robert Fludd who had told him how, in London, printers had demanded a subsidy of £500 and copperplates supplied. Abroad he had been paid £40 and got sixteen free copies. He also found that the quality of production was better on the Continent. As a rule that was probably true, but in fact Harvey's book was not well produced. The paper is poor, the book is full of printing errors, and the plates shown here were not cut specially for this work, but first appeared in Fabricius de Aquapendente's *De venarum ostiolis* from 1603.

William Fitzer, the printer, was born in Broadway *c.*1600. In 1624 he obtained the freedom of the Stationers' Company in London and moved to Frankfurt. In 1625 he married the daughter of one of the wealthy Frankfurt printers, Johann Theodor de Bry. When his father-in-law died in 1626, Fitzer took over the business. The low quality of this book was not merely a reflection of Fitzer's cautious approach to spending money: the Thirty Years' War had made things difficult in Frankfurt, which would not for a long time regain its eminent position in book production and distribution.

Provenance: The Radcliffe Library, after 1749 but before 1835; the collection was transferred to the Bodleian by the Radcliffe Trustees from 1861 to 1893.

Literature: E. Weil, 'William Fitzer the Publisher of Harvey's De motu cordis', *The Library* 24 (1943), 142-64; G. Keynes, *The Life of William Harvey* (Oxford, 1968).

RR. W.168 (plate between pp. 8 and 9)

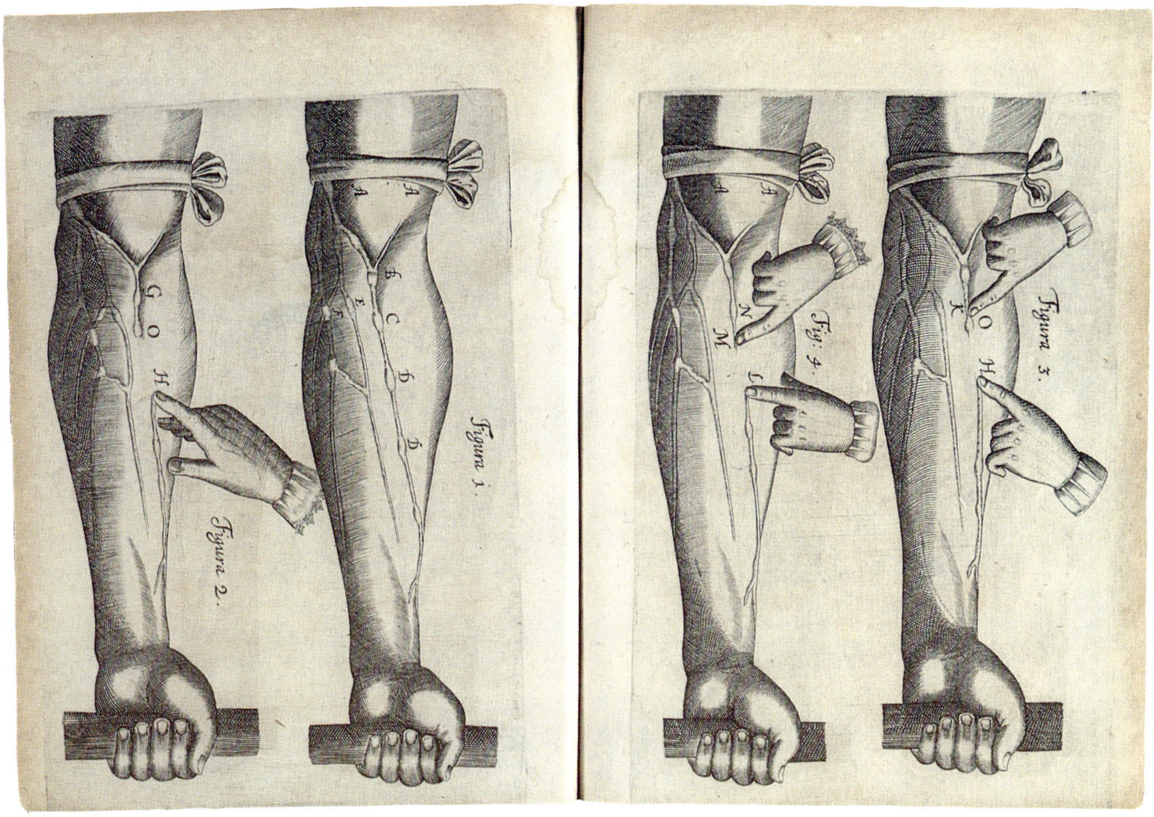
Figura 1.
Figura 2.
Figura 3.
Fig: 4.

International Learning

Art and Science

27 Godfried Bidloo, *Anatomia humani corporis centum et quinque tabulis per G. de Lairesse delineatis demonstrata.*
Amsterdam: widow of Johannes van Someren, heirs of Johannes van Dyk, Henricus Boom and the widow of Theodorus Boom, 1685, 2°.
67 leaves and 105 engraved plates; 625 x 360 mm.

Born in Amsterdam, Bidloo (1649-1713) was appointed Professor of Anatomy at The Hague in 1688, but left soon afterwards to accompany William of Orange to England. In 1690, William III appointed him superintendent of the civil and military hospitals of Holland, and in 1693 the inspector of military hospitals in England. In 1694 he accepted the chair of anatomy at Leiden, but still spent much time in England until William III died in 1702.

After Harvey, the knowledge of human anatomy made rapid progress. While Harvey's work was poorly served by the artistic quality of the secondhand plates that went with it, Bidloo's work on anatomy is best known for its illustrations, which are among the most accomplished copper engravings of the period. In an artistically arranged display, the parts of the human body are shown surrounded by surgical instruments and books, emblematic tools of the surgeon's trade. The plates were designed by Gérard de Lairesse (1641-1711) and possibly engraved by Abraham Blooteling. The many intervening links between the anatomist and the final product indicate that the chief function of the plates was to provide artistic illustration, not to communicate anatomical information. This perception of the function of plates was by now outdated, and his contemporaries criticized Bidloo's work for being anatomically incorrect. In the event the work did not sell well, despite the artistic quality of the illustrations and their concessions to the fashion in Dutch painting for *nature morte*.

Provenance: The Radcliffe Library, after 1749 but before 1835; the collection was transferred to the Bodleian by the Radcliffe Trustees from 1861 to 1893.

Literature: O. Hagelin, *Rare and Important Books in the Karolinska Institute* (Stockholm, 1992), 108-111.

165444 a.29 (plate 71)

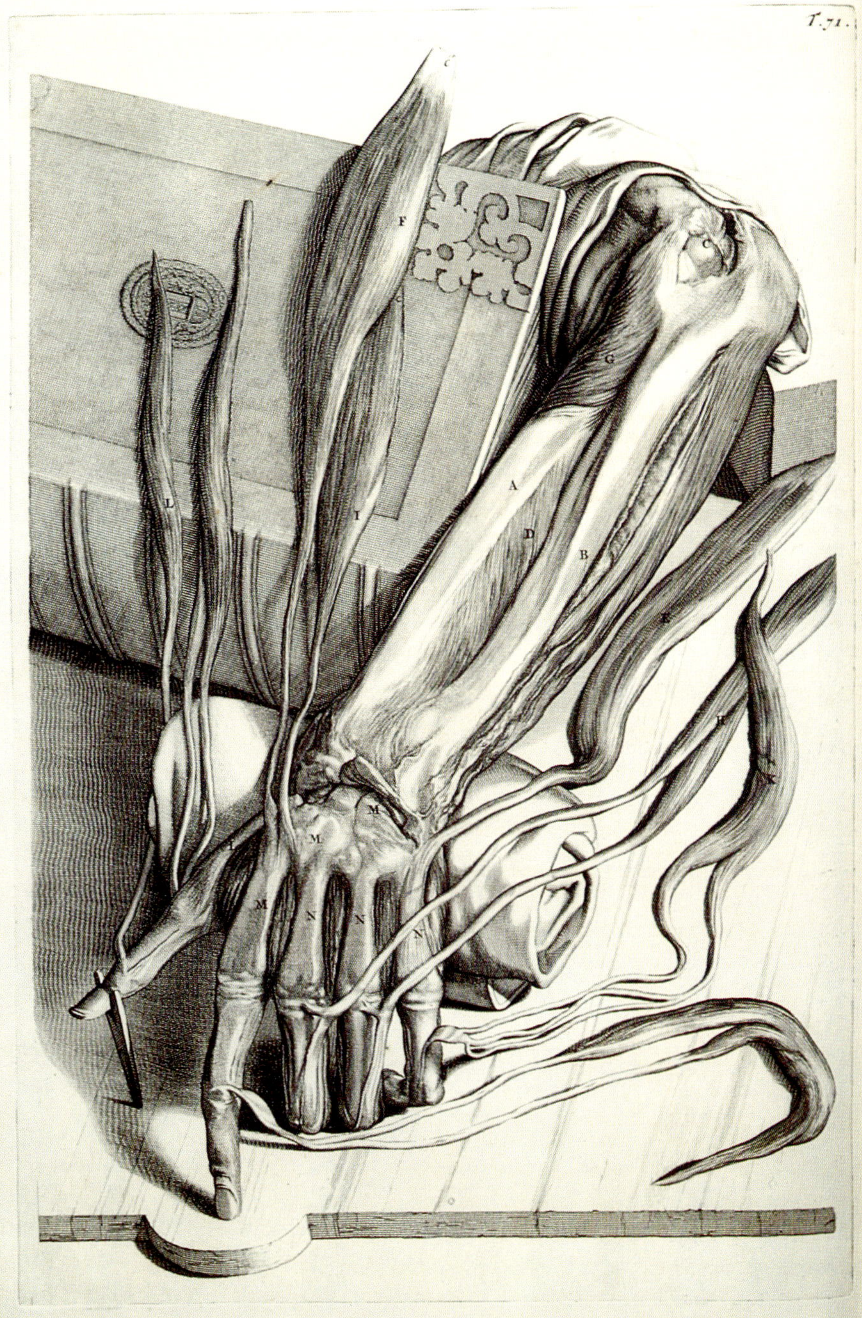
T. 71.
F
G
A
D
B
L
I
M
N

International Learning

Greek Mathematics

28 Euclid, *Elements*.
Constantinople; 888.
iii + 391 leaves; 215 x 180 mm.

In Byzantium there was a relatively continuous tradition of copying and studying ancient Greek authors: the existence of a class of educated laity meant that this activity was not confined to monasteries, as it was in the early medieval West. In relation to this culture the idea of a renaissance, implying a previous demise, may be misleading. Nevertheless, the middle of the 9th century, a period of relative security after the turmoil of preceding centuries, did see a revival of such activity. In *c.*860 the imperial academy was refounded under the direction of Leo, a philosopher and mathematician. At the same period this school was rivalled by the literary activity of Photius, twice Patriarch of Constantinople, whose *Bibliotheca* summarized and commented upon a multitude of pagan and Christian texts.

Scientific and mathematical texts were copied and read as well as the literary and philosophical heritage. Euclid, who taught at Alexandria around 300 BC, was the most prominent mathematician of antiquity. This copy of the *Elements* was finished in September 888 by Stephanus clericus, and bought by Arethas of Patrae (afterwards Bishop of Caesarea in Cappadocia) for fourteen gold coins. Several other books from Arethas's library survive, including the Plato also in the Bodleian (MS. E.D. Clarke 39). The text is written in minuscule, the script (previously used in letters and documents) which began to replace the larger and slower uncial as the standard book-hand during the 9th century. Arethas wrote his marginal scholia in small uncials; the manuscript continued to be used and annotated into the 14th century.

The survival of many Greek texts depended on minuscule manuscripts produced at this period. But, as with many other classical authors, this was not the route by which Euclid reached western Europe: the *Elements* was translated into Latin in the 12th century from Arabic versions encountered in Spain. It remained the primary source of geometric theorems and methods into the 19th century.

Provenance: bought by the Bodleian in 1804 as part of the collection of the Dutch classicist J.P. D'Orville (1696-1751).

Literature: SC 17179; *Survival of Ancient Literature* no. 55; E. Gamillscheg, D. Harlfinger, *Repertorium der griechischen Kopisten 800-1600. I: Handschriften aus Bibliotheken Grossbritanniens* (3 vols: Vienna, 1981), no. 365.

MS. D'Orville 301
(fols. 273v-274r)

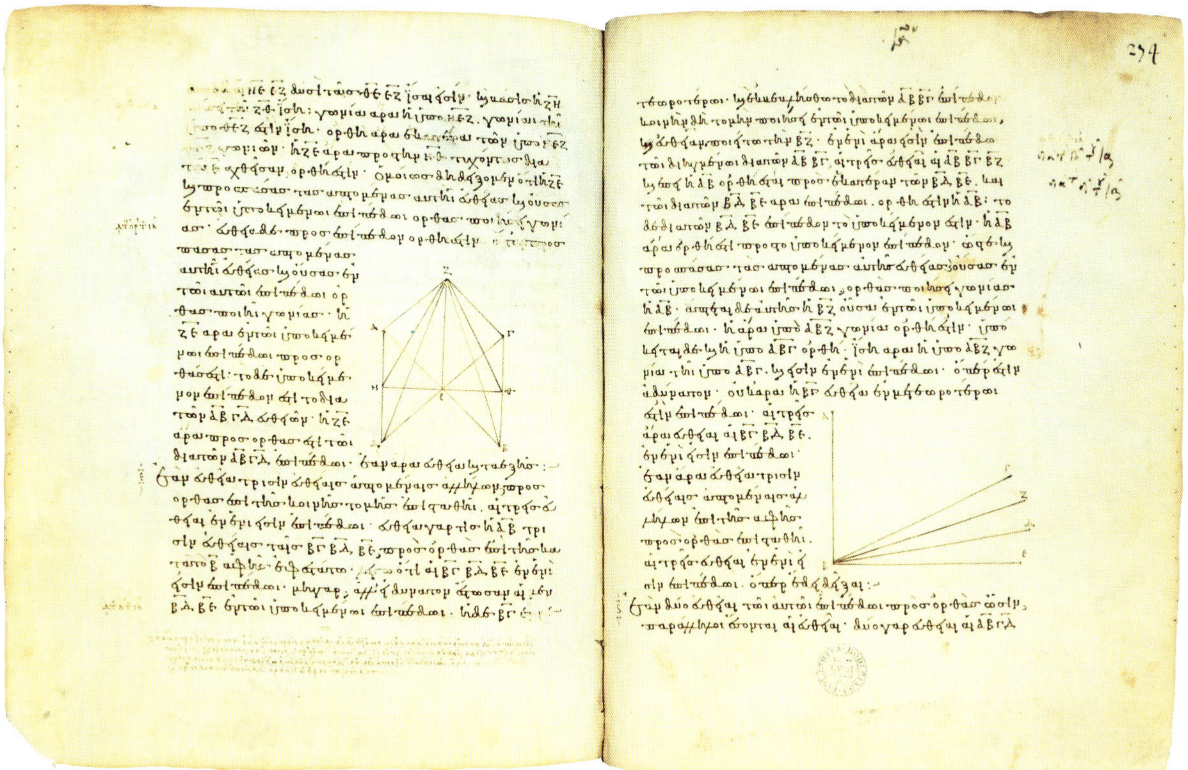

Aristotle

29 Aristotle, *Organon*.
Venice: Aldus Manutius, 1495, 2°. 234 leaves; 310 x 210 mm.

In the West, Greek never achieved the status of Latin as a means of everyday communication between scholars in all fields. It was, nevertheless, from the late 15th century an internationally known language among the best educated in Europe. The most important of all Greek texts in the educational system were those of Aristotle. But Aristotle's texts were not easy to grasp, and readers needed help, either from commentaries or from introductions. Here we show Porphyry's elementary introduction to Aristotle's logic. Porphyry (233- *c*.304) was a Syrian scholar who taught philosophy in Rome. His introduction was much used, particularly in the Latin translation of Boethius. It is here part of the first volume of the first edition of Aristotle's complete works in Greek, printed in Venice in five volumes from 1495 to 1498. The preparation of this edition for the press was a vast collective effort. In a letter of 1497 Aldus Manutius acknowledged the editorial contribution of Thomas Linacre among others. Because of the more restricted readership, the successful publication of a Greek text depended on either very generous patronage, or effective distribution to all seats of learning in Europe, or preferably both. Aldus issued lists of his publications and had a good distribution network which depended on retailers obtaining a reduction in price for buying in quantity. Our copy is in Oxford bindings of the mid-16th century, proof that the volumes came here soon after they were produced.

During the 15th and 16th centuries few, if any, university authors were more frequently printed than Aristotle; but despite the revival of the study of Greek, by far the majority of editions of his works remained Latin translations. The importance of Aristotle in Latin can hardly be overestimated for the creation of a common European vocabulary, not only a technical philosophical vocabulary. Many words which are now considered completely normal are derived from Aristotelian philosophy: words like 'quality', 'quantity', 'form', 'general', and 'special' are based on Latin translations of terminology found in Aristotle's course on logic.

Provenance: in England by the mid-16th century; probably the copy presented to the Bodleian in 1601 by Sir John Fortescue (1531?-1607).

Literature: M. Sicherl, *Handschriftliche Vorlagen der Editio Princeps des Aristoteles* (Abhandlungen der Akademie zu Mainz, Geistes- und Sozialwissenschaftliche Klasse 8: Mainz,1976); *Griechische Handschriften und Aldinen. Eine Ausstellung anläßlich der XV. Tagen der Mommsen-Gesellschaft in der Herzog August Bibliothek Wolfenbüttel* (Wolfenbüttel, 1978), no. 47.

 Auct. 1R 2.2 (sig. Aiiir)

ΠΟΡΦΥΡΙΟΥ ΕΙΣΑΓΩΓΗ.

ΟΝΤΟΣ ἀναγκαίου Χρυσαόριε, καὶ εἰς τὴν τῶν παρὰ Ἀριστοτέλει κατηγοριῶν διδασκαλίαν, τοῦ γνῶναι τί γένος· καὶ τί διαφορά· τί τε εἶδος· καὶ τί ἴδιον· καὶ τί συμβεβηκός· εἴς τε τὴν τῶν ὁρισμῶν ἀπόδοσιν, καὶ ὅλως εἰς τὰ περὶ διαιρέσεως καὶ ἀποδείξεως· χρησίμης οὔσης τῆς τούτων θεωρίας, σύντομόν σοι παράδοσιν ποιούμενος, πειράσομαι διὰ βραχέων ὥσπερ ἐν εἰσαγωγῆς τρόπῳ, τὰ παρὰ τοῖς πρεσβυτέροις ἐπελθεῖν· τῶν μὲν βαθυτέρων ἀπεχόμενος ζητημάτων· τῶν δὲ ἁπλουστέρων συμμέτρως στοχαζόμενος· Αὐτίκα περὶ γενῶν τε καὶ εἰδῶν, τὸ μὲν εἴτε ὑφέστηκεν, εἴτε καὶ ἐν μόναις ψιλαῖς ἐπινοίαις κεῖται, εἴτε καὶ ὑφεστηκότα σώματά ἐστιν, ἢ ἀσώματα· καὶ πότερον χωριστά, ἢ ἐν τοῖς αἰσθητοῖς· καὶ περὶ ταῦτα ὑφεστῶτα, παραιτήσομαι λέγειν· βαθυτάτης οὔσης τῆς τοιαύτης πραγματείας, καὶ ἄλλης μείζονος δεομένης ἐξετάσεως· τὸ δὲ πῶς περὶ αὐτῶν τε καὶ τῶν προκειμένων λογικώτερον οἱ παλαιοὶ διέλαβον, καὶ τούτων μάλιστα οἱ ἐκ τοῦ περιπάτου, νῦν σοι πειράσομαι δεικνύναι·

ΠΕΡΙ ΓΕΝΟΥΣ.

Ἔοικε δὲ μήτε τὸ γένος, μήτε τὸ εἶδος ἁπλῶς λέγεσθαι. γένος γὰρ λέγεται καὶ ἡ τινῶν ἐχόντων πως πρὸς ἕν τι καὶ πρὸς ἀλλήλους ἄθροισις, καθ' ὃ σημαινόμενον, τὸ Ἡρακλειδῶν λέγεται γένος, ἐκ τῆς ἀφ' ἑνὸς σχέσεως, λέγω δὴ τοῦ Ἡρακλέους, καὶ

International Learning

Learning Greek

30 Aesop, *Fabellae.*
Venice: Aldus Manutius, 1505, 4°. 152 leaves; 285 x 170 mm.

Before students could manage Aristotle, the language had to be learned. A number of Latin translations of the fables traditionally ascribed to Aesop had for more than a millennium been standard reading matter for boys learning Latin. It seemed natural to use a version of Aesop's fables in the original language for those who wished to learn Greek. Here we show a bilingual text printed by Aldus Manutius in Venice, using Latin as the medium through which Greek was learned. The facing Latin and Greek texts show how the teaching of Greek was dependent on an assumed knowledge of Latin. The bilingual layout enables a reader to work through Aesop on his own, without a teacher. Beginning with the Latin text, the student will find on the corresponding line on the left-hand side the corresponding Greek text. The reader will even find the relevant Greek word on the same place on the line where the Latin word is also found. The fables shown here are those of the eagle and the fox, and the eagle and the scarab, followed by short summaries of the morals which should be drawn from the fables.

Although Aldus intended his production to be bilingual, the Latin and the Greek texts were printed on separate sheets. This in the end made it impossible to put the book together in such a way that corresponding Greek and Latin texts were presented facing one another throughout the book. In each bilingual gathering Aldus had to break up the flow of the text, and he printed references to guide his reader through the book. He advised more competent readers that they could easily separate out the Latin leaves, and thus restore a straight sequence of fables in Greek.

Provenance: Thomas Barlow (1607-91), Bodley's Librarian 1652-60; bequeathed his copies of printed books not already there to the Bodleian.

 Auct. 1R 3.17 (fols. 24v-25r)

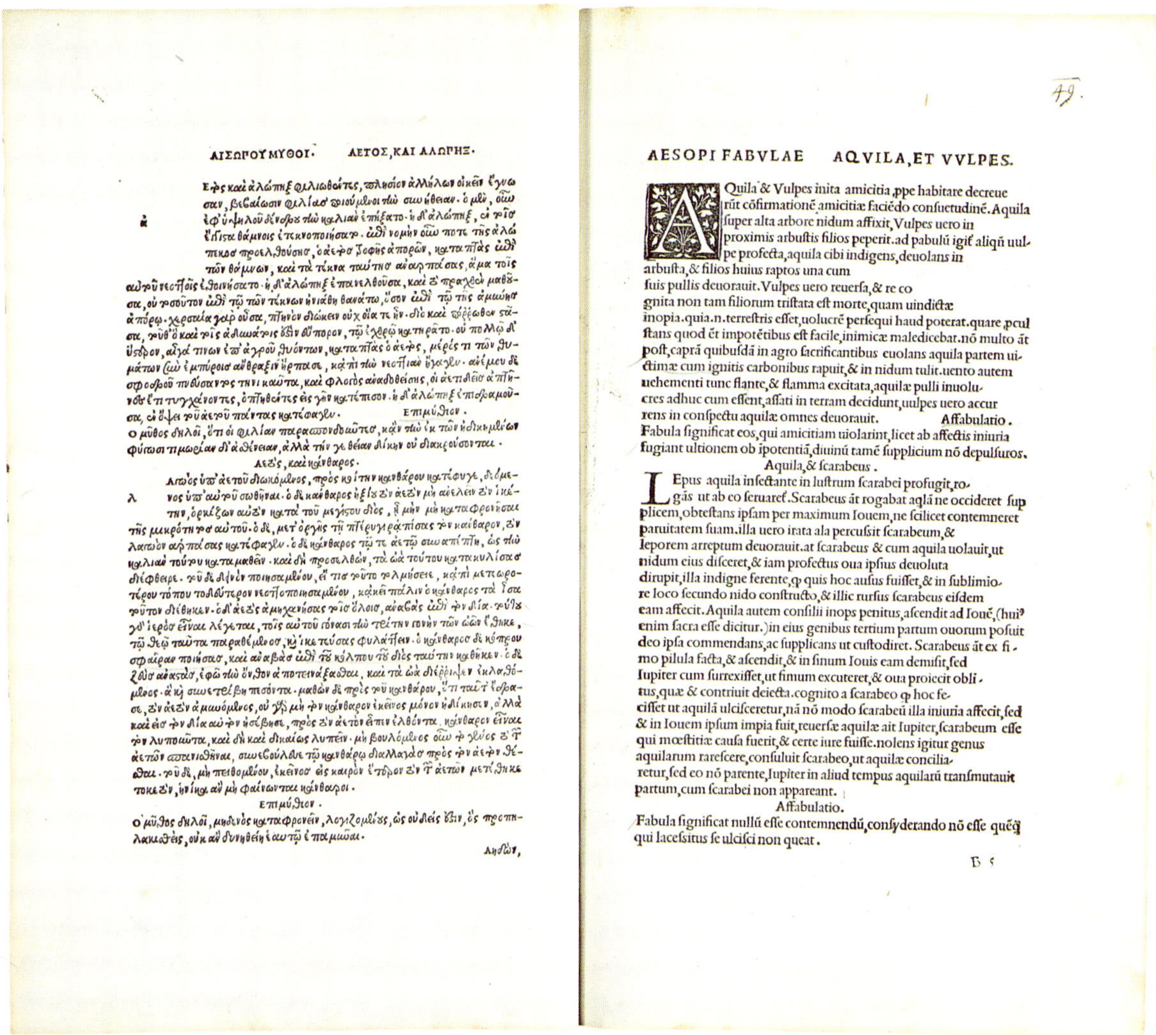

ΑΙΣΩΠΟΥ ΜΥΘΟΙ. ΑΕΤΟΣ, ΚΑΙ ΑΛΩΠΗΞ.

Ἀετὸς καὶ ἀλώπηξ φιλιωθέντες, πλησίον ἀλλήλων οἰκεῖν ἔγνωσαν, βεβαίωσιν φιλίας ποιούμενοι τὴν συνήθειαν. ὁ μὲν οὖν, ἐφ' ὑψηλοῦ δένδρου τὴν καλιὰν ἐπήξατο. ἡ δ' ἀλώπηξ, ἐν τοῖς ἔγγιστα θάμνοις ἐτεκνοποιήσατο. ἐπὶ νομὴν οὖν ποτε τῆς ἀλώπεκος προελθούσης, ὁ ἀετὸς τροφῆς ἀπορῶν, καταπτὰς ἐπὶ τὸν θάμνον, καὶ τὰ τέκνα ταύτης ἀναρπάσας, ἅμα τοῖς αὐτοῦ νεοττοῖς ἐθοινήσατο. ἡ δ' ἀλώπηξ ἐπανελθοῦσα, καὶ τὸ πραχθὲν μαθοῦσα, οὐ τοσοῦτον ἐπὶ τῷ τῶν τέκνων ἠνιάθη θανάτῳ, ὅσον ἐπὶ τῷ τῆς ἀμύνης ἀπόρῳ. χερσαία γὰρ οὖσα, πτηνὸν διώκειν οὐχ οἵα τε ἦν. διὸ καὶ πόρρωθεν στᾶσα, τοῦθ' ὃ καὶ τοῖς ἀδυνάτοις ἐστὶν εὔπορον, τῷ ἐχθρῷ κατηρᾶτο. οὐ πολλῷ δ' ὕστερον, αἶγά τινων ἐπ' ἀγροῦ θυόντων, καταπτὰς ὁ ἀετὸς, μέρος τι τῶν θυμάτων σὺν ἐμπύροις ἄνθραξιν ἥρπασε, καὶ ἐπὶ τὴν νεοττιὰν ἤγαγεν. ἀνέμου δὲ σφοδροῦ πνεύσαντος τηνικαῦτα, καὶ φλογὸς ἀναφθείσης, οἱ ἀετιδεῖς ἄπτηνες ἔτι τυγχάνοντες, ὀπτηθέντες εἰς γῆν κατέπεσον. ἡ δ' ἀλώπηξ ἐπιδραμοῦσα, ἐν ὄψει τοῦ ἀετοῦ πάντας κατέφαγεν. Ἐπιμύθιον.

Ὁ μῦθος δηλοῖ, ὅτι οἱ φιλίαν παρασπονδοῦντες, κἂν τὴν ἐκ τῶν ἠδικημένων φύγωσι τιμωρίαν δι' ἀσθένειαν, ἀλλὰ τήν γε θείαν δίκην οὐ διακρούσονται.

Ἀετὸς, καὶ κάνθαρος.

Λαγωὸς ὑπ' ἀετοῦ διωκόμενος, πρὸς κοίτην κανθάρου κατέφυγε, δεόμενος ὑπ' αὐτοῦ σωθῆναι. ὁ δὲ κάνθαρος ἠξίου τὸν ἀετὸν μὴ ἀνελεῖν τὸν ἱκέτην, ὁρκίζων αὐτὸν κατὰ τοῦ μεγίστου Διὸς, ἦ μὴν μὴ καταφρονῆσαι τῆς μικρότητος αὐτοῦ. ὁ δὲ, μετ' ὀργῆς τῇ πτέρυγι ῥαπίσας τὸν κάνθαρον, τὸν λαγωὸν ἁρπάσας κατέφαγεν. ὁ δὲ κάνθαρος τῷ τε ἀετῷ συναπέπτη, ὡς τὴν καλιὰν τούτου καταμαθεῖν. καὶ δὴ προσελθὼν, τὰ ᾠὰ τούτου κατακυλίσας διέφθειρε. τοῦ δὲ δεινὸν ποιησαμένου, εἴ τις τοῦτο τολμήσειε, καὶ ἐπὶ μετεωροτέρου τόπου τὸ δεύτερον νεοττοποιησαμένου, κἀκεῖ πάλιν ὁ κάνθαρος τὰ ἴσα τοῦτον διέθηκεν. ὁ δ' ἀετὸς ἀμηχανήσας τοῖς ὅλοις, ἀναβὰς ἐπὶ τὸν Δία, τούτου γὰρ ἱερὸς εἶναι λέγεται, τοῖς αὐτοῦ γόνασι τὴν τρίτην γονὴν τῶν ᾠῶν ἔθηκε, τῷ θεῷ ταῦτα παραθέμενος, καὶ ἱκετεύσας φυλάττειν. ὁ κάνθαρος δὲ κόπρου σφαῖραν ποιήσας, καὶ ἀναβὰς ἐπὶ τὸν κόλπον τοῦ Διὸς ταύτην καθῆκεν. ὁ δὲ Ζεὺς ἀναστὰς, ἐφ' ᾧ τὴν ὄνθον ἀποτινάξασθαι, καὶ τὰ ᾠὰ διέρριψεν ἐκλαθόμενος. ἃ καὶ συνετρίβη πεσόντα. μαθὼν δὲ παρὰ τοῦ κανθάρου, ὅτι ταῦτ' ἔδρασε, τὸν ἀετὸν ἀμυνόμενος, οὐ γὰρ μὴ τὸν κάνθαρον ἐκεῖνος μόνον ἠδίκησεν, ἀλλὰ καὶ εἰς τὸν Δία αὐτὸν ἠσέβησε, πρὸς τὸν ἀετὸν ἐπανελθόντα, κάνθαρον εἶναι τὸν λυποῦντα, καὶ δὴ καὶ δικαίως λυπεῖν. μὴ βουλόμενος οὖν τὸ γένος τῶν ἀετῶν σπανισθῆναι, συνεβούλευε τῷ κανθάρῳ διαλλαγὰς πρὸς τὸν ἀετὸν θέσθαι. τοῦ δὲ, μὴ πειθομένου, ἐκεῖνος εἰς καιρὸν ἕτερον τὸν τῶν ἀετῶν μετέθηκε τοκετὸν, ἡνίκα ἂν μὴ φαίνωνται κάνθαροι.

Ἐπιμύθιον.

Ὁ μῦθος δηλοῖ, μηδενὸς καταφρονεῖν, λογιζομένους, ὡς οὐδείς ἐστιν, ὃς προπηλακισθεὶς, οὐκ ἂν δυνηθείη ἑαυτῷ ἐπαμῦναι.

Ἀηδών,

49.

AESOPI FABVLAE AQVILA, ET VVLPES.

AQuila & Vulpes inita amicitia, ꝓpe habitare decreuerũt cõfirmationẽ amicitiæ faciẽdo consuetudinẽ. Aquila super alta arbore nidum affixit, Vulpes uero in proximis arbustis filios peperit. ad pabulũ igiť aliqñ uulpe profecta, aquila cibi indigens, deuolans in arbusta, & filios huius raptos una cum suis pullis deuorauit. Vulpes uero reuersa, & re cognita non tam filiorum tristata est morte, quam uindictæ inopia. quia .n. terrestris esset, uolucrẽ persequi haud poterat. quare ꝓcul stans quod ẽt impotẽtibus est facile, inimicæ maledicebat. nõ multo ãt post, caprã quibusdã in agro sacrificantibus euolans aquila partem uictimæ cum ignitis carbonibus rapuit, & in nidum tulit. uento autem uehementi tunc flante, & flamma excitata, aquilæ pulli inuolucres adhuc cum essent, assati in terram decidunt, uulpes uero accurrens in conspectu aquilæ omnes deuorauit. Affabulatio.

Fabula significat eos, qui amicitiam uiolarint, licet ab affectis iniuria fugiant ultionem ob ĩpotentiã, diuinũ tamẽ supplicium nõ depulsuros.

Aquila, & scarabeus.

LEpus aquila insectante in lustrum scarabei profugit, rogãs ut ab eo seruareť. Scarabeus ãt rogabat aqlã ne occideret supplicem, obtestans ipsam per maximum Iouem, ne scilicet contemneret paruitatem suam. illa uero irata ala percussit scarabeum, & leporem arreptum deuorauit. at scarabeus & cum aquila uolauit, ut nidum eius disceret, & iam profectus oua ipsius deuoluta dirupit, illa indigne ferente, ꝙ quis hoc ausus fuisset, & in sublimiore loco secundo nido constructo, & illic rursus scarabeus eisdem eam affecit. Aquila autem consilii inops penitus, ascendit ad Iouẽ, (huiꝰ enim sacra esse dicitur.) in eius genibus tertium partum ouorum posuit deo ipsa commendans, ac supplicans ut custodiret. Scarabeus ãt ex fimo pilula facta, & ascendit, & in sinum Iouis eam demisit, sed Iupiter cum surrexisset, ut fimum excuteret, & oua proiecit oblitus, quæ & contriuit deiecta. cognito a scarabeo ꝙ hoc fecisset ut aquilã ulcisceretur, nã nõ modo scarabeũ illa iniuria affecit, sed & in Iouem ipsum impia fuit, reuersæ aquilæ ait Iupiter, scarabeum esse qui mœstitiæ causa fuerit, & certe iure fuisse. nolens igitur genus aquilarum rarescere, consuluit scarabeo, ut aquilæ conciliaretur, sed eo nõ parente, Iupiter in aliud tempus aquilarũ transmutauit partum, cum scarabei non appareant.

Affabulatio.

Fabula significat nullũ esse contemnendũ, consyderando nõ esse queꝗ qui lacessitus se ulcisci non queat.

B 5

International Learning

Greek Printers

31 Simplicius, *Ὑπόμνημα εἰς τὰς δέκα κατηγορίας τοῦ Ἀριστοτέλους.* Venice: Zacharias Kallierges for Nicolaos Vlastos, 1499, 2°. 168 leaves; 335 x 220 mm.

A great number of Greeks from Venetian Greek possessions, and refugees from the Turkish expansion, lived in Venice. Exploiting the position of the city as the most important centre of distribution, much of the early printing of Greek took place there. This book was produced by a Greek resident in Venice and Padua, where he worked both as a scribe and as a printer. Kallierges (*c.*1473-after 1524), a nobleman born in Rethimnon in Crete, began printing in Venice together with Nicolaos Vlastos. The most famous work from their press was perhaps the *Ἐτυμολογικὸν μέγα* of 1499. Here we show the first page of another of their works from 1499, Simplicius's commentary on Aristotle's *Categories*. Simplicius was a teacher at the Platonic Academy in Athens. As part of his policy of enforced Christianisation, Justinian, Emperor of the East, issued an edict banning non-Christians from all teaching positions. The school in Athens was closed in 529 and its considerable endowments were confiscated. With some other teachers Simplicius attempted to continue their school in the Persian Empire, but the experiment failed and Simplicius returned to the Roman Empire around 533. This commentary stems from after his return when any teaching he may have done would have had to be done in secrecy. While Porphyry (no. 29) provided a beginners' aid to Aristotle's logic, this commentary provides advanced observations on the text. Simplicius's commentaries were important in 15th- and 16th-century philosophical circles, not least in neighbouring Padua whose university was the centre of a lively Aristotelian debate. The border and the initial letter demonstrate another way in which printers of early books tried to reproduce features which are now most often associated with manuscripts. As shown by for instance the Würzburg missal (no. 19), it was common to leave out initials for them to be added by hand. Gutenberg had already experimented with printing large initials in red, and most often Kallierges followed this principle. But Kallierges experimented with other ways of imitating manuscript features in print. Here we show a page with an elaborate decoration printed in gold leaf, using a technique which is not yet entirely explained. The green and red, however, were added by hand.

Provenance: Nicolaus Leonicus Thomæus (1456-1531); James Ludovic Lindsay, 26th Earl of Crawford (1847-1903): Crawford sale 19 June 1889, no. 105; John Gennadius (1844-1932): Gennadius sale 28 March 1895, no. 112 for £12.5.0; Ingram Bywater (1840-1914): bequeathed to the Bodleian in 1914.

Literature: V. Carter, L. Hellinga, T. Parker, 'Printing with Gold in the Fifteenth Century', *The British Library Journal* 9 (1983), 1-13; P & A ii, no. pr.110.

 Byw. A 3.16(2) (fol. 2r)

ΝΙΚΟΛΑΟΥ ΤΟΥ ΒΛΑΣΤΟΥ

ΣΧΟΛΙΑ ΕΙΣ ΤΑΣ ΑΡΙΣΤΟΤΕΛΟΥΣ ΚΑΤΗΓΟΡΙΑΣ, ΑΠΟ ΦΩΝΗΣ ΣΙΜΠΛΙΚΙΟΥ ΔΙΔΑΣΚΑΛΟΥ ΜΕΓΑΛΟΥ.

Πολλοὶ πολλὰς κατεβάλοντο φροντίδας, εἰς τὸ τῶν κατηγοριῶν τοῦ ἀριστοτέλους βιβλίον. οὐ μόνον ὅτι προοίμιόν ἐστι τῆς ὅλης φιλοσοφίας, εἴπερ αὐτὸ μὲν τῆς λογικῆς ἐστιν ἀρχὴ πραγματείας. ἡ δὲ λογικὴ τῆς ὅλης παραλαμβάνεται δικαίως φιλοσοφίας, ἀλλὰ καὶ ὅτι τρόπον τινὰ περὶ ἀρχῶν ἐστι τῶν πρώτων, ὡς ἐν τοῖς περὶ τοῦ σκοποῦ μαθησόμεθα λόγοις. ἄλλοι δὲ κατ᾽ ἄλλην ὁρμὴν τὰς περὶ τοῦτο τὸ βιβλίον πραγματείας πεποίηνται. οἱ μὲν, αὐτὴν μόνην τὴν λέξιν ἐπὶ τὸ σαφέστερον μεταθεῖναι προθυμηθέντες. ὥσπερ θεμίστιός τε ὁ εὐφραδὴς, καὶ εἴ τις ἄλλος τοιοῦτος. οἱ δὲ, καὶ τὰς ἐννοίας μὲν, αὐτὰς δὲ μόνας ψιλὰς τὰς ὑπὸ τοῦ ἀριστοτέλους προτεινομένας, συντόμως ἀποκαλύπτειν ἐσπούδασαν. ὥσπερ ἐν τῷ κατὰ πεῦσιν καὶ ἀπόκρισιν βιβλίῳ πεποίηκεν ὁ πορφύριος. ἄλλοι δὲ πρὸς τούτοις, καὶ ζητημάτων ἐφήψαντο μετρίως, ὡς ὁ ἀφροδισιεὺς ἀλέξανδρος, καὶ ἑρμῖνος, καὶ ὅσοι τοιοῦτοι. ὧν καὶ μάξιμον ἐγὼ τίθημι, τὸν αἰδεσίου μὲν τοῦ ἰαμβλίχου μαθητήν. ἐν δὲ τῷ εἰς τὰς κατηγορίας ὑπομνήματι, πάντα σχεδὸν τῷ ἀλεξάνδρῳ συνάσαντα. τινὲς μέχρι καὶ βαθυτέραις περὶ αὐτὸ διανοίαις ἐχρήσαντο, ὥσπερ ὁ θαυμάσιος βοηθός. ἄλλοις δὲ ἤρεσεν ἀπορίας μόνας γράψαι πρὸς τὰ λεγόμενα. ὅπερ λούκιός τε πεποίηκε, καὶ μετ᾽ αὐτὸν νικόστρατος, τὰ τοῦ λουκίου ὑποβαλλόμενος. σχεδὸν τι πρὸς πάντα τὰ εἰρημένα κατὰ τὸ βιβλίον, ἐνστάσεις κομίζειν φιλοτιμούμενοι. καὶ οὐδὲ εὐλαβῶς, ἀλλὰ καταφορικῶς μᾶλλον, καὶ ἀπηρυθριακότως. πλὴν καὶ τούτοις χάρις. καὶ ὅτι πραγματειώδεις τὰς πολλὰς τῶν ἀποριῶν προεβάλοντο, καὶ ὅτι λύσεώς τε τῶν ἀποριῶν ἀφορμὰς, καὶ ἄλλων πολλῶν τε καὶ καλῶν θεωρημάτων τοῖς μετ᾽ αὐτοὺς ἐκδεδώκασι. πλωτῖνος δὲ ὁ μέγας ἐπὶ τούτοις, τὰς πραγματειωδεστέρας ἐξετάσεις, ἐν τρισὶν ὅλοις βιβλίοις τοῖς περὶ τῶν γενῶν τοῦ ὄντος ἐπιγεγραμμένοις, τῷ τῶν κατηγοριῶν βιβλίῳ προσήγαγε. μετὰ δὲ τούτους, ὁ πάντων ἡμῖν τῶν καλῶν αἴτιος πορφύριος, ἐξήγησίν τε ἐντελῆ τοῦ βιβλίου, καὶ τῶν ἐνστάσεων πασῶν λύσεις οὐκ ἀπόνως ἐν ἑπτὰ βιβλίοις ἐποιήσατο, τοῖς γεδαλίῳ προσφωνηθεῖσι. πολλὰ καὶ τῶν στωϊκῶν ἐκ δογμάτων κατὰ τὴν κοινωνίαν τοῦ λόγου προσιστορῶν. μετὰ

Α β

International Learning

Hebrew

32 Jacob ben Asher, *'Arba 'ah Ṭûrîm.*
Constantinople: David and Samuel ibn Nahmias, 13 Dec. 1493.
2°, 408 leaves; 305 x 210 mm.

Provenance: the first known owner was from the eastern part of the Mediterranean: two inscriptions, in a 16th- or early 17th-century Sephardic hand, mention the same person, one giving his name in the Hebrew style: 'In the name of the beloved boy, the favourite child Abraham, son of Eliah, son of Isaac'; the other in the Arabic style, 'Ibrahim ibn the honoured [Eliah] ibn Ishaq Elkahan, may the Lord bless him and protect him etc. until the end of all generations, Amen.' The second known owner wrote his name in an Ashkenazi, Germanic, hand from the late 17th or early 18th century: 'Uri Feywesh ben Joseph, may he live long and happily, Amen' [inscriptions kindly read by A. K. Offenberg]; acquired, probably between 1727 and 1733, by David Oppenheim, chief Rabbi in Prague (d. 1735), who was compelled to keep his library in Hannover, outside the Holy Roman Empire; the library passed to his son, a Rabbi in Heidelberg; bought, with the entire library of David Oppenheim, by the Bodleian in 1829 from Isaac Seligmann, bookseller in Hamburg.

The third international language in Europe was Hebrew, known and used by Jews who were resident in most European countries. The Spanish period of exploration and expansion coincided with the expulsion from Spain of all non-Christian elements, the Muslims and, in 1492, the Jews. The expansion of Europe coincided with a delimitation against its non-Christian inhabitants and neighbours.

This is the first book printed in the Ottoman Empire, 'The Four Orders' — a commentary on the Hebrew code of law — printed by two Jewish refugees from Spain. David and Samuel ibn Nahmias were probably brothers who left with a group of refugees from Valencia on 31 July 1492, finally obtaining asylum in Naples some time after 22 September 1492. By 1492 Jewish printers in the city states of Italy were obstructed to such an extent that only Naples provided safety for the printing of Hebrew. But soon it became impossible for Jews to be active as printers even in Naples. For a while a single Jewish printer survived in hiding, printing in hamlets and villages, but Jewish printing in Italy came to an end in 1497, the year in which the Jews were expelled from Portugal. The main type used in this book comes from Naples. Probably David and Samuel ibn Nahmias took it with them when they left. The paper, however, comes from northern Italy, which was normal for paper used in Constantinople. Contacts between Constantinople and Venice in particular were close and frequent.

Literature: A. K. Offenberg, 'The First Printed Book Produced at Constantinople (Jacob ben Asher's 'Arba 'ah Ṭûrîm, December 13, 1493)', *Studia Rosenthaliana* 3 (1969), 96-112; *idem, A Choice of Chorals, Facets of Fifteenth-Century Hebrew Printing* (Nieuwkoop, 1992), 102-131.

Opp. fol. 724 (fol. 408r, the colophon)

ויהרגהו ומיהו כל אדם בחוק' זה הוא ויכול להורגו אלא
אם כן יודע שהיותר אוהב לבעל הממון ולא יהרגנו אף
אם יעמוד נגדו להציל ממונו וכן אם האב חותר על הבן
מסתמא אין להורגו כי רחמי האב על בנו ולא יהרגנו אף
אם יעמוד כנגדו להציל ממונו אלא אם כן ידוע שהאב ש
שונא את הבן ויהרגנו אם יעמוד הבן כנגדו להציל ממונו
כתב הרמב"ם אחד הבא במחתרת או שמצאו בתוך גגו ש
של אדם או בתוך חורבתו או בתוך קרפיפו בין ביום בין
בלילה ולמה נאמר מחתרת לפי שדרך רוב גנבים לבא ב
במחתרת בלילה אבל הבא במחתרת בתוך שדהו או לתוך
הדיר והסהר יש לו דמים שחזקתו שבא על הממון לבד ל
לפי שאין רוב הבעלים מצוין במקומות אילו וכן הגנב ש
שגנב ויצא מן המחתרת הואיל ופנה עורף יש לו דמים. ו
וכן אם הקיפוהו עדים או בני אדם אעפ' שעדין הוא ברש
ברשות זה שבא עליו אינו נהרג ואין צריך לומר שאם תב
תבעו בבית דין שאינו נהרג עד כאן והראב"ד כתב אעפ'
שדרשו חכמים אם זרחה עליו דרך משל מכל מקום אין מ
מקרא יוצא מידי פשוטו וביום אינו רשאי להורגו שאין ג
גנב בא ביום אלא דרך השמטה שומט וברח מיד ואינו
מתעכב לגנוב ממון גדול ולא לעמוד על בעלים להורגו א
אלא גנב בלילה מפני שיודע שבעל הבי' בבית ובא להורגו
או ליהרג אבל גנב יום אין בעל הבי' מצוי בביתו ושמיטה
בעלמא הוא עד כאן ומטעם זה גם כן יש לומר דאפילו ב
בלילה דוקא בא במחתרת כיון שחותר דעתו להרוג בעל
הממון אבל דרך גגו או חצר יש לומר שאין דעתו להרוג
בעל הממון אלא אם יעמוד כנגדו בורח מפני שלא נכנס
לביתו אלא מפני שמצא דרך ליכנס כמו שאמרו חכמים
פרצה קוראה לגנב הבא על הבעיא מי שמקנא לנסם יכול
להורגו אבל אם בא לבית דין לישאל אין מורין לו להורגו א

אבל אם הוא כשנאו יקנא לבו כחטאים וירצה להורגו ה
הרשות בידו ודוקא בשעת מעשה ובפרהסיא אבל כשבא
או שפירש הבועל אין המקנא רשאי להורגו ואפילו אם ל
לא פירש והרג הוא למקנא אינו נהרג עליו הרג אדם את'
למקנא נהרג עליו ומיני ישראל והם שעובדים לע"ז ואפיק
ואפיקורסין והם שכופרין בנבואה ובתורה שבעל פה וה
והעוברין על אחת מכל המצות להכעיס מורידין אותן ש
שאין הרואה יש בו כח להורגו בפרהסיא יעשה ואם לאו
יבא עליו בעלילה כיצד נפל לבור ויש סולם בבור ישלקנו
בעלילה שיאמר לו הריני צריך להעלות בני מן הגג וכן כל
כיוצא בזה אבל הרועים בהמה דקה וכיוצא בהם אילו שעו
שעוברין עבירות תמיד אין מורידין אותם לבור לסבב מ
מיתתו אבל אם ירדו לבור אינו צריך להעלותו שנ' לא ת
תעמוד על דם רעך והאי לאו ריע הוא במה דברים אמ
אמורים במי שהוא בעל עבירות ועומד ברשעו ושונה בו
כגון הרועים שפקרו בהם ושונים בגזלתם אבל מי שאינו
עומד ברשעו אלא אוכל נבלות או עובר על שאר עבירות
להנאתו אסור לעמוד על דמו ומצוה להצילו

תכח

הרואה את חבירו טובע בנהר או שלסטי'
באין עליו חייב להצילו בין בגופו בין במו
בממונו ומיהו אם יש לו ממון להציל עצמו חייב לשלם לזה
והרמב"ם כתב הרואה שחבירו טובע בנהר או שלסטין ב
באין עליו ויכול להצילו או שישכור אחרים להצילו או שש
ששמע שגוים או מוסרין מחשבין עליו רעה או גילה לאזנ'
חבירו והודיעו או שידע בגוי או באנס שהוא קובל על ח
חבירו ויכול הוא לפייסו בגלל חבירו ולהוציא שטנה מלבו
ולא פייס וכל כיוצא בזה עובר על לא תעמוד על דם רעך
ואם מציל כאילו קיים עולם

א כדברי יראי ה' איש אשר עזו ויקשב ה' וישמע ויכתב בספר זכרון לפניו בהתנדב עם לחזק בדק הדת ולהושיבה
האמונה על מכונה כי ה' חפץ למען צדקו יגדיל תורה ויאדיר: הוי כל צמא לכו למים ואשר אין לו כסף התבוננות
לשבור מהתלמוד להוציא לאור דין האיסור והיתר והחיוב והפטור והטהרה והמותר מצד טורח הגלות כי ארכו
לו שם הימים לכן שברו בלא טורח יין התורה וחלבה מהספר הזה הנכבד ד' טורים מחברת החכם הר"ר
יעקב בן הר"ר אשר וכו תשאבו מי הדיינים בששון מגלתי נער לבחור האמת מתפכו ולעשות אזכבם
כמרכבת כי טבחו טבוח וייכו מזוג הלכה רווחת מצרף לכסף החיוב והפטור וכור לזהב
האיסור וההתר ולהיות שראיתי תועלת זה הספר ואת יקר תפארת גדולתו משאר
ספרי הפוסקים כי הדור ראוי לכך השתדלנו להרבין תורה בישראל על
יד האומנים ר' דוד' בן נחמיאש ור' שמואל אחיו תהי משכורתם
שלמה כי יש שכר לפעולתם להיותם סבת המצוה

ככר נתבאר זה כל היה קורא בברכות והשתדלתי בהשלמתו בחסרת הטעות כפי האיפשר אני הדל באלפי אלאה בכ'הר'
בנימין הלוי נ"ע ואמנם להיות שמחוק זאת המלאכה להעתק חלקיה מיד אל יד לא ינקה כל מכונה בה מהשגיאה אמנם ר
רק ההשתדלות בחוק האיפשר הוא שלמות מצד מה גם אמר נעים זמירות ישראל שגיאות מי יבין ולהיות שכבר) כתבאר
בפ' מצטרפין בשקלים ופ' האשה שהלך בעלה ביבמות ת"ח האומר דבר הלכה מפיו בעולם הזה שפתיו דובבות כו' אומר
על כד הבחות והסיון שהיתה השלמת אלו הטורים פרשת ויחי רוח יעקב אביהם יום ו' ד' לטבת שנת חמשת אלפים ומ
ומאתים וחמשים וארבעה פה בעיר קוסטנטינא רבתי תחת מלכות ישמעאל המלך הגדול שולטן בייזיט יחי לעד יחי א'
בעזרו ותנשא מלכותו אמן

International Learning

Philology and the Bible

33 Complutensian Polyglot.
Alcalá de Henares, 1514 [-1522], 2°. Vol. 3, 204 leaves; 360 x 260 mm.

The expulsion of the Jews from many European countries in the late 15th century coincided with an increased interest in the study of the Hebrew language. This study was to gain prominence in the Protestant countries of northern Europe where the greatest importance was attached to the understanding of the texts of the Bible, and where all clergy were later to be required to read Hebrew. However, a significant contribution was made to Christian Hebrew Biblical scholarship in Spain before the religious divisions of 16th-century Europe.

The Complutensian Polyglot Bible takes its name from Complutum, the Latin name for Alcalá de Henares. A monument to pre-reformation philology, it was financed by the cardinal Francisco Ximenes de Cisneros (1426-1517), and edited by amongst others Diego López de Zúñiga (d. 1531) and Antonio de Lebrija (1444-1522). It was also a typographical landmark. Here we have four versions of the Psalms, in three different languages, printed side by side on the same leaf. We show the beginning of the Psalms of David, with the Hebrew original in the right-hand column, then Jerome's translation into Latin from the Hebrew, and finally the Greek translation of the Septuagint, with an interlinear Latin translation: Jerome's translation from the Septuagint. The Greek of the Old Testament was printed with accents, as here. But the Greek of the New Testament was printed without accents. An introduction claims that this was derived from ancient practices and that a modern rendering should be as faithful as possible to the original, as it was written by the Holy Ghost. This meant excluding accents. Humanist philological arguments were used to overturn tradition in order to get closer to the word of the Holy Ghost. Only a few years later such arguments would have been considered dangerously controversial.

Provenance: given to a Spanish Jesuit College in the early 17th century; bought in 1663 by Frater Innocentius Pencini, using alms given to him, for the Dominican convent of SS Giovanni e Paolo in Venice; bought from Henry Sotheran in 1906 by Ingram Bywater; bequeathed by Bywater to the Bodleian in 1914.

Literature: Anejo a la edición facsímile de la Biblia políglotta complutense (Valencia, 1987); Á. Sáenz-Badillos, La filología bíblica en los primeros helenistas de Alcalá (Estella, 1990); [K. Jensen], Printing Greek: A European Enterprise: An Exhibition at the Bodleian Library (Oxford, 1992), no. 17.

 Byw. B 3.5 (fol. 79r)

Trās. Gre. lxx. cū interp. latina. Trāsla. B. Hie. Tex. heb. ps. i. ii. iii. Pritiua. he·

PSALTERIVM.
ΨΑΛΤΗΡΙΟΝ.

Psalm⁹ dauid: sine titulo apud hebreos. 1.
Ψαλμὸς τῷ δαυίδ, ἀνεπίγραφος παρ᾽ ἑβραίοις. ά.
Beatus vir q̄ nō abijt in cōsilio ipioꝝ:
Μακάριος ἀνὴρ ὃς οὐκ ἐπορεύθη ἐν βουλῇ ἀσεβῶν,
et in via pctoꝝ nō stetit: ⁊ in cathedra
καὶ ἐν ὁδῷ ἁμαρτωλῶν οὐκ ἔστη, καὶ ἐπὶ καθέδρα
pestilētie nō sedit. Sed in lege dn̄i volū
λοιμῶν οὐκ ἐκάθισεν. Ἀλλ᾽ ἢ ἐν τῷ νόμῳ κυρίου τὸ θέλη
tas eius: ⁊ in lege ei⁹ meditabit die ac nocte.
μα αὐτοῦ, καὶ ἐν τῷ νόμῳ αὐτοῦ μελετήσει ἡμέρας καὶ νυκτός.
Hiere. 17.b. Et erit tanq̄ lignū qd plātatū est secus decursus
Καὶ ἔσται ὡς τὸ ξύλον τὸ πεφυτευμένον παρὰ τὰς διεξόδους
aquaꝝ. qd fructū suū dabit in tpe suo:
τῶν ὑδάτων, ὃ τὸν καρπὸν αὐτοῦ δώσει ἐν καιρῷ αὐτοῦ,
Et foliū eius nō defluet: ⁊ oīa q̄cunq̄
Καὶ τὸ φύλλον αὐτοῦ οὐκ ἀπορρυήσεται, καὶ πάντα ὅσα ἂν
faciet: psperabūtur. Non sic ipij nō sic
ποιῇ, κατευοδωθήσεται. Οὐχ οὕτως οἱ ἀσεβεῖς οὐχ οὕ-
sed tanq̄ puluis quē pijcit vētus a facie
τως, ἀλλ᾽ ἢ ὡσεὶ χνοῦς ὃν ἐκρίπτει ὁ ἄνεμος ἀπὸ προσώπου
terre. Ideo nō resurgēt ipij in iudicio:
τῆς γῆς. Διὰ τοῦτο οὐκ ἀναστήσονται ἀσεβεῖς ἐν κρίσει,
neq̄ pctōres in cōsilio iustoꝝ. Qm̄ nouit dn̄s viā iu
οὐδὲ ἁμαρτωλοὶ ἐν βουλῇ δικαίων. Ὅτι γινώσκει κς ὁδὸν δι
stoꝝ: ⁊ iter ipioꝝ peribit. Psalmus dauid. 2.
καίων, καὶ ὁδὸς ἀσεβῶν ἀπολεῖται. Ψαλμὸς τῷ δαδ΄. β΄.
Actuū 4.c. Quare fremuerūt gētes ⁊ ppl̄i: meditati sūt inania?
Ἱνατί ἐφρύαξαν ἔθνη καὶ λαοί, ἐμελέτησαν κενά;
Astiterūt reges terre: ⁊ pncipes cōuene-
Παρέστησαν οἱ βασιλεῖς τῆς γῆς, καὶ οἱ ἄρχοντες συνήχθη
rūt in vnū: aduersus dn̄m ⁊ aduersus xp̄m
σαν ἐπὶ τὸ αὐτό, κατὰ τοῦ κυρίου καὶ κατὰ τοῦ χριστοῦ
eius. Dirūpamus vincula eoꝝ: ⁊ pijciamus
αὐτοῦ. Διαρρήξωμεν τοὺς δεσμοὺς αὐτῶν, καὶ ἀπορρίψω
a nobis iugū ipsoꝝ. Qui habitat in celis irride-
μεν ἀφ᾽ ἡμῶν τὸν ζυγὸν αὐτῶν. Ὁ κατοικῶν ἐν οὐρανοῖς ἐκγελά
bit eos: ⁊ dn̄s subsānabit eos. Tūc lo
σεται αὐτούς, καὶ ὁ κύριος ἐκμυκτηριεῖ αὐτούς. Τότε λα
q̄tur ad eos in ira sua: ⁊ in furore suo cō
λήσει πρὸς αὐτοὺς ἐν ὀργῇ αὐτοῦ, καὶ ἐν τῷ θυμῷ αὐτοῦ τα
turbabit eos. Ego āt cōstitut⁹ sū rex ab eo sup
ράξει αὐτούς. Ἐγὼ δὲ κατεστάθην βασιλεὺς ὑπ᾽ αὐτοῦ ἐπὶ
Heb. 1.b. syō montē sanctū ei⁹: pdicās pceptū dn̄i. Dn̄s
σιὼν ὄρος τὸ ἅγιον αὐτοῦ, διαγγέλλων τὸ πρόσταγμα κυ. Κύριος
Actu. 13.c. dixit ad me: fili⁹ me⁹ es tu: ego hodie genui te. Po
εἶπε πρός με, υἱός μου εἶ σύ, ἐγὼ σήμερον γεγέννηκά σε. Αἴ-
Apo. 2 g. ⁊. 19 c. stula a me: et dabo tibi gētes hereditatē tuā: ⁊
τησαι παρ᾽ ἐμοῦ, καὶ δώσω σοι ἔθνη τὴν κληρονομίαν σου, καὶ
possessionē tuā terminos terre. Reges eos in
τὴν κατάσχεσίν σου τὰ πέρατα τῆς γῆς. Ποιμανεῖς αὐτοὺς ἐν
virga ferrea: tanq̄ vasa figuli cōfringes eos. Et
ῥάβδῳ σιδηρᾷ, ὡς σκεύη κεραμέως συντρίψεις αὐτούς. Καὶ
nūc reges itelligite: erudimini oēs q̄ iudicatis
νῦν βασιλεῖς σύνετε, παιδεύθητε πάντες οἱ κρίνοντες τὴν
terrā. Seruite dn̄o in timore: ⁊ exultate ei
γῆν. Δουλεύσατε τῷ κυρίῳ ἐν φόβῳ, καὶ ἀγαλλιᾶσθε αὐτῷ
in tremore. Apphēdite disciplinā: nequādo irascat dn̄s: ⁊ pe-
ἐν τρόμῳ. Δράξασθε παιδείας, μήποτε ὀργισθῇ κς, καὶ ἀπο
reatis de via iusta. Cum exarserit in breui ira e-
λεῖσθε ἐξ ὁδοῦ δικαίας. Ὅταν ἐκκαυθῇ ἐν τάχει ὁ θυμὸς αὐ-
ius: beati oēs q̄ cōfidūt in eo.
τοῦ, μακάριοι πάντες οἱ πεποιθότες ἐπ᾽ αὐτῷ.
Psalmus dauid: cū fugeret a fa
Ψαλμὸς τῷ δαυίδ, ὁπότε ἀπεδίδρασκεν ἀπὸ προ
cie absalom filij sui. 3.
σώπου ἀβεσσαλὼμ τοῦ υἱοῦ αὐτοῦ. γ.
Domie q̄d multiplicati sūt q̄ tribulāt me? multi
Κύριε τί ἐπληθύνθησαν οἱ θλίβοντές με; πολλοὶ
insurgūt aduersū me: multi dicūt aie mee: nō
ἐπανίστανται ἐπ᾽ ἐμέ, πολλοὶ λέγουσι τῇ ψυχῇ μου, οὐκ
est salus ipsi in deo eius. dp.
ἔστι σωτηρία αὐτῷ ἐν τῷ θεῷ αὐτοῦ. Διάψαλμα.

Incipit liber psal-
morum. 1.
Beatus vir qui non abijt in consilio impiorum: & in via peccatorum non stetit: & in cathedra derisorū non sedit. Sed in lege domini voluntas eius: & in lege eius meditabitur die ac nocte. Et erit tanq̄ lignum transplātatum iuxta riuos aq̄rum: quod fructū suū dabit in tpe suo: & folium eius non defluet: & omne quod fecerit prosperabitur. Nō sic impii: sed tanquā puluis quem proiicit ventus. Propterea non resurgent impii in iudicio: neq̄ peccatores in cōgregatione iustorum. Quoniam noscit dn̄s viam iustorum: & iter impiorum peribit. 2.
Quare congregauerunt gentes: & tribus meditabuntur inania. Consurgent reges terre: & principes tractabūt pariter: aduersus dn̄m & aduersus xp̄m eius. Dirumpamus vincula eorum: & proiiciamus a nobis laqueos eorum. Habitans in celis irridebit: dominus subsannabit eos. Tūc loquetur ad eos in ira sua: & ī furorē suo cōturbabit eos. Ego autem ordinaui regē meum: super sion mōtē sctm̄ meū. Annunciabo dei preceptū: dn̄s dixit ad me filius meus es tu: ego hodie genui te. Postula a me & dabo gentes hereditatem tuam: & possessionem tuam terminos terre. Franges eos in virga ferrea: vt vas figuli conteres eos. Et nunc reges intelligite: erudimini iudices trē. Seruite dn̄o in timore: & exultate ī tremore. Adorate pure: ne forte irascatur & pereatis de via: cum exarserit post paululū furor eius: bti oēs q sperant ī eū.
Psalm⁹ dd̄ cū fugeret a facie absalō filii sui. 3.
Domine q̄re multiplicati sunt hostes mei: m̄lti cōsurgūt aduersum me. Multi dicunt anime mee: nō est salus huic in deo. Sp.

אשרי האיש אשר לא הלך
בעצת רשעים ובדרך חטאים לא
עמד ובמושב לצים לא ישב:
כי אם בתורת יהוה חפצו
ובתורתו יהגה יומם ולילה: והיה
כעץ שתול על פלגי מים אשר
פריו יתן בעתו ועלהו לא יבול
וכל אשר יעשה יצליח: לא כן
הרשעים כי אם כמץ אשר
תדפנו רוח: על כן לא יקמו
רשעים במשפט וחטאים בעדת
צדיקים: כי יודע יהוה דרך
צדיקים ודרך רשעים תאבד:
ii. למה רגשו גוים ולאמים
יהגו ריק: יתיצבו מלכי
ארץ ורוזנים נוסדו יחד על יהוה
ועל משיחו: ננתקה את
מוסרותימו ונשליכה ממנו
עבתימו: יושב בשמים ישחק
אדני ילעג למו: אז ידבר אלימו
באפו ובחרונו יבהלמו: ואני
נסכתי מלכי על ציון הר קדשי:
אספרה אל חק יהוה אמר אלי
בני אתה אני היום ילדתיך:
שאל ממני ואתנה גוים נחלתך
ואחזתך אפסי ארץ: תרעם
בשבט ברזל ככלי יוצר תנפצם:
ועתה מלכים השכילו הוסרו
שפטי ארץ: עבדו את יהוה
ביראה וגילו ברעדה: נשקו בר
פן יאנף ותאבדו דרך כי יבער
כמעט אפו אשרי כל חוסי בו: iii.
מזמור לדוד בברחו מפני אבשלום
בנו: יהוה מה רבו צרי רבים
קמים עלי: רבים אמרים לנפשי
אין ישועתה לו באלהים סלה:

a

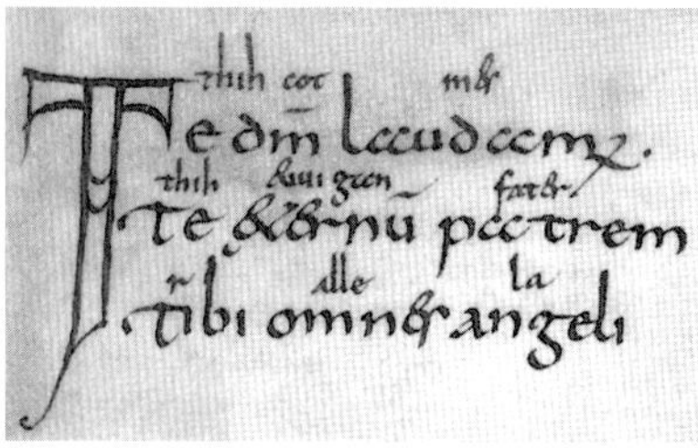

Vernaculars across Europe

Dissimilar as they may appear, European vernaculars make up a discernible unity when seen from the outside. A shared cultural and historical experience has ensured that in most European languages words and expressions are found for identical concepts, which can often be expressed only with difficulty in languages which have not been exposed to European cultural influence. This vernacular unity was created in part through the use of the same texts, through adopting the same words from Latin, the most frequent procedure in the Romance languages and in English, or from making a translation component by component, the most frequent procedure in the Germanic languages. The unifying impact of the works of antiquity on the European vernaculars is evident in all fields of learning. Here this is illustrated by the translation of Vitruvius (no. 46); a similar process in the area of natural history is visible in the works of Conrad Gesner (no. 25).

The most basic forms of translation (no. 35) are found in glossaries, lists of individual words, and in word-for-word translations of texts, which often cannot be read independently of the original, because they make no concession to the syntax of the vernacular. In some cases we can see the development towards more idiomatic translation, with the vernacular text becoming readable in its own right (no. 38). Less literal translations, however, could create problems for a society in which texts were viewed as authoritative. The most obvious example of this is the Bible: while translations of selected passages were useful for religious instruction (no. 36), translations of the complete text could create controversy. The success of a translation depended on the level of authority ascribed to the translator or the group of translators: a translation could be outlawed by association (no. 38). But a Biblical translation which lacked official sanction could nonetheless gain unofficial diffusion (nos 38, 39).

Not all common features of the vernacular literatures of Europe derived from the shared inheritance of classical and religious texts. Vernacular literatures also drew upon a shared tradition of oral literature. Epic poems recounting heroic deeds were part of this literary tradition. By the nature of things, our exhibition can only show works which were already leaving the world of oral literature, but it seems that our manuscript of the *Chanson de Roland* (no. 40) is close to one of the points where oral and written literatures meet. Written in French in England, this manuscript indicates how vernaculars did not coincide with nation states. This point is reinforced by a book of troubadours' songs from Italy (no. 41) but written in Provençal, a language used for this genre by writers whose own vernacular may have been Italian or Catalan.

Similar cycles of stories were recounted in many European vernaculars. To a modern reader this poses the question of when a work is a translation and when it should be counted as a new work: in a society where tradition was more important than innovation, the implication that it was somehow inferior to rely on a well known story would have seemed incomprehensible. Boccaccio's stories and their translations illustrate the way a theme could be developed in transmission from one language to another (no. 43). Firmly established in the written tradition of story-telling and of knightly romance is *Don Quixote* (no. 44), which was soon a success throughout Europe: a common reservoir of genres and themes created a European literary community across the boundaries of our vernaculars.

Vernaculars across Europe

Hagiography

34 Maghnus Ó Domhnaill (Magnus O'Donnell), *Betha Coluim Cille* (Life of St. Columba).
Lifford Castle, Co. Donegal; 1532.
iii + 81 leaves; 425 x 285 mm.

St. Columba (*c.*521-97) founded the monasteries of Derry, Durrow, and (perhaps) Kells before leaving Ireland with twelve companions for the island of Iona, which was to be his base for missionary work in Scotland. The O'Donnells claimed kinship with the saint: the compilation of sources for his life was an act of piety, scholarship, and dynastic propaganda. In his preface Magnus explains that he wanted to translate the Latin biographical material (principally the Life by Adomnan) into Irish, and to render intelligible everything concerning the saint which had been preserved in earlier (and by then obscure) vernacular literature. This family copy also contains the bardic poems written for the O'Donnells over several centuries, and is in its contemporary binding - no less vernacular in its way than the language of the text - of sealskin on boards, with corner-pieces of bronze. The production of such a volume at the family seat of the patron represented the revival of an Irish tradition which had declined during the political troubles of the period.

The text is prefaced by an arresting full-length 'portrait' of the saint in abbatial vestments - archaic by contemporary European standards, but in this context an innovative blend of representational art with native abstract elements. By contrast the script is an entirely traditional formal hand - though the arrangement in paragraphs may be a reflection of the layout of printed books. Whereas the Norman Conquest to a great extent marked the end of vernacular art forms in Ireland, the same is not true of script and manuscript decoration. The monasteries formed by the Normans imported books and had them copied in the same style; but professional Irish scribes continued to use the traditional Insular scripts - developed in Ireland and Britain between the 7th and 9th centuries, after the Roman withdrawal from Britain - into the 19th century.

Provenance: Sir James Ware (1594-1666); Henry Hyde, second Earl of Clarendon (1638-1700); James Brydges, first Duke of Chandos (1673-1744); bequeathed by Richard Rawlinson (1690-1755).

Literature: Quarto cat. V, part I, cols. 733-4; eds. A. O'Kelleher, G. Schoepperle, *Betha Colaim Chille (Life of Columcille). Compiled by Manus O'Donnell in 1532* (with translation) (Irish Foundation Series 1: Urbana, Illinois, 1918); P & A iii, no.1288; F.J. Byrne, *A Thousand Years of Irish Script. An Exhibition of Irish Manuscripts in Oxford Libraries* (Bodleian Library, 1979), no. 18.

MS. Rawl. B. 514
(fol. iii verso)

Vernaculars across Europe

Glossing and Glossaries

35 'The Murbach Hymnal'.
Germany; late 8th and 9th centuries.
iii + 197 leaves; 280 x 185 mm (width varies between sections).

This composite manuscript contains two important types of evidence for the vernacular as an aid to the reading of Latin. The page reproduced shows the word-by-word glossing of a Latin text - in this case the pre-Carolingian monastic hymnal, containing the hymns sung in the monastic offices throughout the year. Twenty-one out of the repertoire of twenty-six hymns found here were probably written at the abbey of Reichenau in the early 9th century, and then taken to the abbey of Murbach in Alsace, where five more were added not much later, perhaps also copied from a Reichenau exemplar. Over each line of the Latin text an Old High German translation is written in a smaller script. The gloss was not intended to be read independently: in some places only the endings of the German words are provided, in order to elucidate syntactical relationships in the Latin. The aim was not to produce a vernacular translation, but to understand the Latin text.

The other type of evidence found here is the glossary - a list of difficult Latin words with their equivalents in the vernacular. Of the three main glossaries contained here, now named after the philologist who gave the manuscript to Oxford, 'Junius A' lists the words in the order of the texts in which the compiler encountered them (including Genesis, Exodus, and some non-Biblical material); whilst in 'Junius B' and 'Junius C', the Latin words are grouped by their initial letters - though within these groups they are not arranged in strict alphabetical order. Although it is possible to see them in terms of a typological development, it is likely that all three glossaries were used for study, not for reference in the way that a modern dictionary is used.

By 1461, when it was restored at Murbach, the separate booklets of this compilation had certainly been gathered together: they may all have been collected much earlier. Apart from the items of vernacular interest, the contents include the *Cosmographia* of 'Aethicus Ister', Alcuin's *De Rhetorica* and *De Dialectica*, and expositions of the Creed and the Lord's Prayer.

Provenance: Marcus Zuerius Boxhorn (1612-53); Isaac Vossius (1618-89); Francis Junius (1589-1677), who gave his collection to Oxford University in the year of his death.

Literature: ed. E. Sievers, *Die Murbacher Hymnen* (Halle, 1874); SC 5137; P & A i, nos 1, 4, 5, 22; N. Henkel, *Deutsche Übersetzungen lateinischer Schultexte* (Munich, 1988), 68-72.

 MS. Junius 25 (fol. 117v)

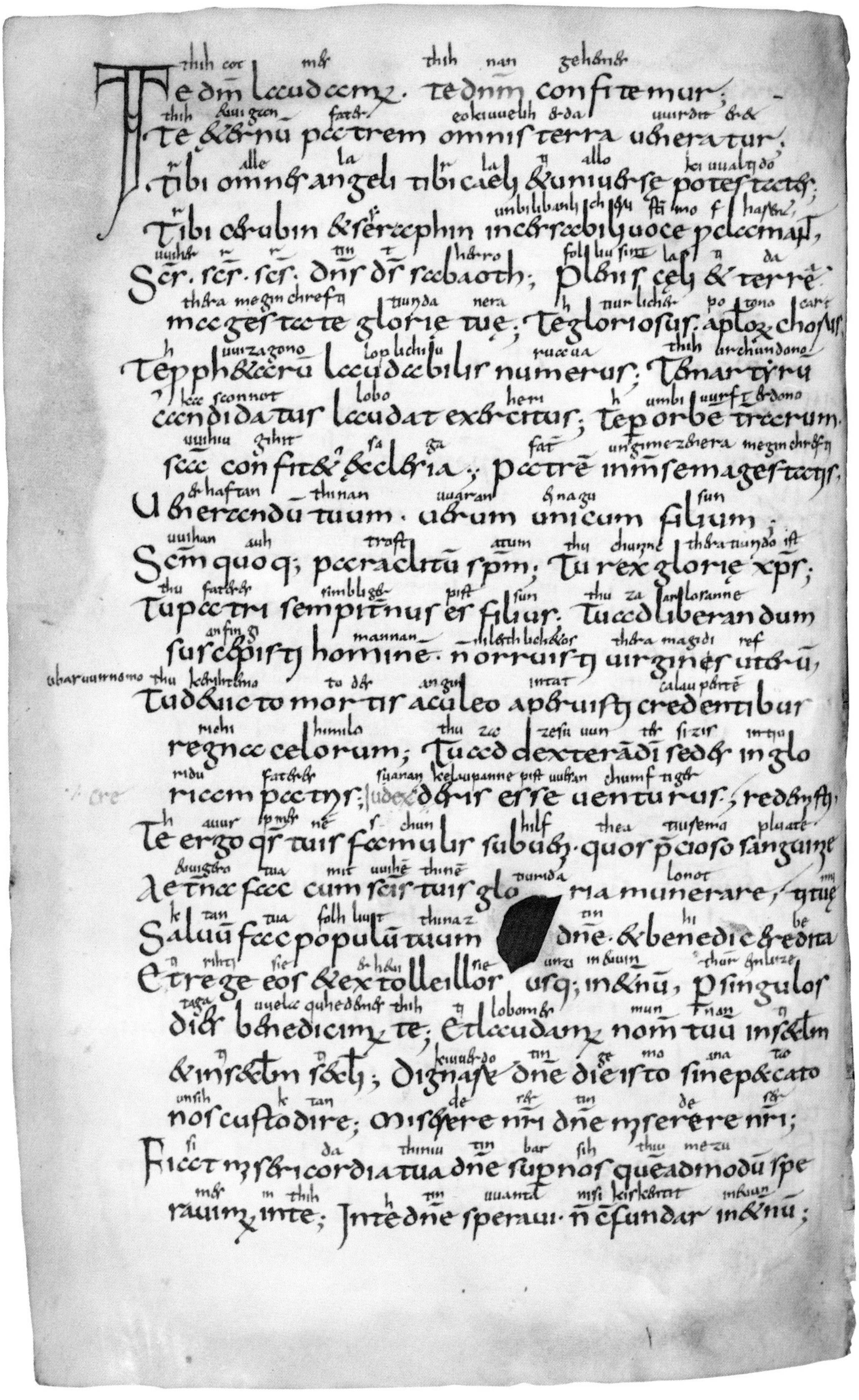

Te dm laudamus. te dnm confitemur;
Te aeternu patrem omnis terra ueneratur;
Tibi omnes angeli tibi caeli & uniuersae potestates;
Tibi cherubin & seraphin incessabili uoce proclamant;
Scs. scs. scs. dns ds sabaoth; pleni sunt caeli & terrae
maiestatis gloriae tuae; Te gloriosus apostolorum chorus
Te prophetaru laudabilis numerus; Te martyru
candidatus laudat exercitus; Te per orbe terrarum
sca confitetur aecclesia; patre inmensae maiestatis;
Uenerandu tuum uerum unicum filium;
Scm quoq; paraclitu spm; Tu rex gloriae xpe;
Tu patris sempiternus es filius; Tu ad liberandum
suscepisti hominem. non horruisti uirginis uteru;
Tu deuicto mortis aculeo aperuisti credentibus
regna caelorum; Tu ad dexteram di sedes in glo
ria patris; Iudex crederis esse uenturus; [illegible]
Te ergo quaes tuis famulis subueni quos p̄tioso sanguine
redemisti. aeterna fac cum scis tuis glo ria munerare;
Saluu fac populu tuum [damaged] dne & benedic hereditati
tuae; Et rege eos & extolle illos usq; in aetnu. Per singulos
dies benedicimus te; Et laudamus nom tuu in saeclm
& in saeclm saecli; Dignare dne die isto sine peccato
nos custodire; Miserere nri dne miserere nri;
Fiat misericordia tua dne sup nos quemadmodu spe
rauimus in te; In te dne speraui. n̄ confundar in aetnu;

Vernaculars across Europe

Vernacular Biblical Instruction

36 Apocalypse. Blockbook.
Germany, *c.*1465-70, 48 leaves printed on one side only, interleaved with 24 leaves of manuscript text written on both sides; 290 x 215 mm.

Blockbooks are printed, not from movable type, but from woodblocks: in this case one block was used for printing two pages. The woodcuts are hand coloured. The sequence of pictures gives an account of the events which — according to the Book of Revelations — will precede the end of the world. Each illustration contains an excerpt from the Bible. Top right is the text from Apocalypse 13. 2-4, continued in the first line in the text bottom right. The other texts are commentaries. The seven-headed beast, having come out of the sea, gives its power to the dragon which is then adored.

Provenance: presented to an ecclesiastical institution in Germany by Diether V. von Handschuhsheim (1430-87); presented to the University in 1638 by William Laud (1573-1645), Archbishop of Canterbury.

The production, distribution and readership of blockbooks are controversial topics. In addition to the pictures and the texts within them, our copy contains a German translation in manuscript. Recent research has found that nine copies of Apocalypse blockbooks exist which are accompanied by a manuscript text in a central German dialect. The German texts of these nine copies are related, but not identical. This suggests that at least some blockbooks were meant by their producers to be bilingual, and it poses questions about the relation between vernacular languages and Latin. It seems clear that among the owners of blockbooks there was a need for vernacular texts: perhaps not entirely ignorant of Latin, they probably found German easier. It seems unlikely that the German text was intended to have the didactic function of the Latin text which accompanied the Greek of the Aesop in no. 30, or of the German glosses to the Latin in the Murbach Hymnal (no. 35). This book was probably meant for lay instruction in the events leading up to the end of the world, rather than theological study.

Literature: W. L. Schreiber, *Manuel de l'amateur de la gravure sur bois et sur métal au XVe siècle*, vol. 4 (Leipzig, 1902), 164-65; N. Palmer, 'Latein und Deutsch in die Blockbüchern', in *Latein und Volkssprache im deutschen Mittelalter 1100-1500. Regensburger Colloquium 1988* (Tübingen, 1992), eds. N. Henkel, N. Palmer, 310-36, describing our copy as of Edition IV E; *Die Apokalypse Blochbuch-Ausgabe IV E Mainz, Gutenberg-Museum, Ink. 131, Farbmikrofiche-Edition*, ed. E. Purpus (Munich, 1991).

The Apocalypse blockbooks are derived from a tradition of medieval English Apocalypse manuscripts. In comparison, the quality of these woodcuts is indifferent and the colouring crude. This might be taken as an argument against a highly sophisticated group of readers, especially in Germany where woodcuts were produced to such high standards. Professor Nigel Palmer has recently noted that the our copy was given to an unnamed religous institution by Diether V. von Handschuhsheim (1430-87); this might hint at a background in circles around the court in Heidelberg.

Auct. M 3.15 (printed leaf 25: Schreiber, p. 119, block no. 23 (25))

Der drach das ist der tufel der alle sin macht
hatt gegeben dem tier. das ist dem endecrist
der doch zu mal boss ist | wan er wont in jme
vnd was der tufel bossheit erdencken kan | wirckt
er gantz durch jne vnd die sieben houpter des
endecrists | das sint die sieben todsund vnd das
houpt was zu sehen als ob es by na ab gesniten
were | vnd doch nit zu male | das bezeichent
die sunde der gantzen welt vnd jr vspotting

Der drach gab jme sin krafft vnd gross macht
vnd sant Johans sach der houpt eins | das by nach
ab geschnitten was bis in dot | vnd die plag
des tods ist wider vmb genesen | des hat
sich verwondert die gantz welt von dem
gruwlichen tiere.

Vnd sie haben angebeten den drachen dem
der dem gruwlichen tier | sin macht
hat gegeben | vnd haben doch nit ange-
beten den drachen | sonder sie haben ange-
beten den tufel | des sie nit ensahen | vnd
haben dar durch angebetten den endecrist
der by der erden wirt bezeichent | vnd by
dem endecrist der tufel | vnd sprachen das
niemant mocht glich sin dem endecrist
oder siner sterck wider stan

Vernaculars across Europe

Vernacular Evangelization

37 Slavonic Gospels.
Neamțu, Moldavia; 1429.
315 leaves; 310 x 220 mm.

The creation of a Slavonic alphabet is traditionally credited to Cyril, who with his brother Methodius led a mission from Constantinople to the Moravian Slavs in the early 860s. In fact he was probably responsible for the formalization of the Glagolitic alphabet developed by the Slavs (perhaps out of cursive Greek) during the previous two centuries. The Cyrillic alphabet, based on uncial Greek, was probably adapted by Cyril's disciples, who perceived Glagolitic as unsuitable for religious books. Remarkably, Cyril's translation of the Gospels into the vernacular gained official acceptance in Constantinople in 863 - though the rendering of the liturgy into the vernacular was subsequently to become the cause of dispute.

The colophon on fol. 312r identifies Princess Marina, the third wife of Prince Alexander the Good of Moldavia, as the patron of the book, and the monk Gavril as its scribe. The Bulgarian Church Slavonic text is written in uncial script: each Gospel begins with a decorated headpiece, gold title, and decorated initial. The pericopes, or liturgical readings, are marked in the text, and their appointed days are given in the margins. The parallel Greek text was added in the margins in the late 16th or early 17th century. Moldavia (which joined Walachia to form the state of Romania in 1859) was an independent principality at this period; but Byzantine influence continued in all types of artistic production, and is evident here in the Evangelist portrait preceding each Gospel.

Provenance: Matteo Luigi Canonici (1727-*c.*1806); bought by the Bodleian as part of the Canonici collection, 1817.

Literature: Quarto cat. I, part II, col. 105; E. Turdeanu, 'The Oldest Illuminated Moldavian Manuscript', *Slavonic and East European Review* 29 (1951), 456-69; R. Cleminson, *A Union Catalogue of Cyrillic Manuscripts in British and Irish Collections* (London, 1988), no. 158.

MS. Canon. Gr. 122
(fols. 89v-90r)

Vernaculars across Europe

Vernacular Heresy

38 Wycliffite Bible.
England; late 14th century?
i + 334 leaves; 330 x 230 mm.

In 15th-century England, the translation of the Bible was forbidden. Archbishop Arundel's Constitutions of 1407 also made it an offence to possess an existing translation, unless it dated from before the time of Wycliffe or had been licensed by the diocesan authorities. But more copies survive of the Wycliffite Bible than of any other medieval text in English. The idea of translating Scripture was not necessarily heretical: at the very beginning of the century, the question could be debated openly at Oxford without the immediate suggestion of heresy. Yet it was soon to become a question of authority: 'Just as Wyclif himself put forward many views that originated in orthodox circles, which became outlawed because of their association with his heterodox opinions on topics such as the Eucharist, so many opinions later identified with Lollardy could be questions of neutrality in the early years of the movement'(Hudson).

This manuscript is a copy of the 'Earlier Version' of the Old Testament up to Baruch 3.20. The literal, almost word-for-word rendering of the Latin Vulgate into English (more akin to the glossing of no. 35 than to translation) was subsequently made more fluent and idiomatic in the interests of intelligibility. MS. Bodl. 959 contains the most literal text of the Earlier Version, but even here the early stages of modification can be seen in the numerous corrections by several hands. The process of revision was complex, and involved intensive study of the Latin text: the scale of the project suggests that it was a collaborative effort, probably to be placed in the last two decades of the 14th century. Once established, the 'Later Version' superseded the Earlier, and circulated widely.

The scholarly attitude to the text and concern for accessibility are reflected in the high quality and uniform presentation of the surviving manuscripts. Outside the books themselves, however, there is little evidence for the circumstances of Lollard book production. Evidence for the ownership of this and other vernacular texts is provided by the records of Lollard trials, which reveal the high value set by the movement upon literacy and instruction.

Provenance: given to the Bodleian in 1602.

Literature: SC 3093; M. Deanesly, *The Lollard Bible and Other Medieval Biblical Versions* (Cambridge, 1920); ed. C. Lindberg, *MS Bodley 959. Genesis-Baruch 3.20 in the Earlier Version of the Wycliffite Bible* (Stockholm Studies in English 6, 8, 10, 13, 20: Stockholm, 1959-73); A. Hudson, *The Premature Reformation: Wycliffite Texts and Lollard History* (Oxford, 1988), 238-47.

MS. Bodl. 959 (fol. 233v)

Vernaculars across Europe

Translators in Exile

39 *The Bible and Holy Scriptures Contayned in the Olde and Newe Testament.* Geneva: Rowland Hall, 1560, 4°. 616 leaves; 235 x 160 mm.

The Reformation provided the vernacular languages of northern Europe with an important boost. Controversies were written in vernaculars to gain wider support, and translations of the Bible proliferated. As with scientific texts, vernaculars were not there ready for the translators to use. Vernacular words had to be created for terms and concepts for which words had not previously been in common use, and translators had to acquaint themselves with aspects of their vernaculars with which they were themselves not familiar (see also nos 25 and 46).

The close contacts of English reformers with the rest of reformed Europe were reinforced by the reimposition of Roman Catholicism during the reign of Mary Tudor, under whom many went into exile in Protestant countries. Among them were the parents of Sir Thomas Bodley, who took their young son with them to the Continent. Here we show the 'Geneva Bible'. It was produced in Geneva by English religious refugees who had not yet returned after the accession of Queen Elizabeth, to whom the volume is dedicated. The Geneva Bible had a background in Calvinist Geneva, but was not explicitly Calvinist in its notes and in details of translation. The international nature of Protestant Bibles is here emphasised by the illustrations, which occur in the book of Exodus only, depicting the implements of the tabernacle. They are based on — much more accomplished — illustrations first made for the Bible produced by the French Calvinist Henri Estienne, and used in many later Bibles with a Calvinist background.

On 8 January 1561, a seven-year printing privilege on the text of the Geneva Bible was granted to Sir Thomas Bodley's father, John, who, although he had returned to England in 1558, retained his contacts with his associates in Geneva. It was never the authorized version, but at least 140 editions were printed in London between 1560 and 1644.

Provenance: despite the financial interest of the Bodley family in the Geneva Bible, Sir Thomas's library did not contain a copy of it for many years. The Geneva Bible was not for the learned, but mainly for use in the home: given 1679, by his mother, to William Edbrooke of Exeter College, Oxford; Joseph Powell, 1690s; probably acquired by the Bodleian in the 19th century.

Literature: T. H. Darlow, H. F. Moule, *Historical Catalogue of the Printed Editions of the Holy Scripture*, vol. 1 (London, 1903), 61.

Bib. Eng. 1560 d.1
(fols. 35v-36r)

thereof: that is, two rings *shalbe* on ŷ one
side of it, and two rings on the other si-
de thereof.
13 And thou shalt make barres of Shittim
wood, and couer them with golde.
14 Then thou shalt put the barres in the
rings by the sides of the Arke, to beare ŷ
Arke with them.

THE ARKE OF THE TESTIMONIE.

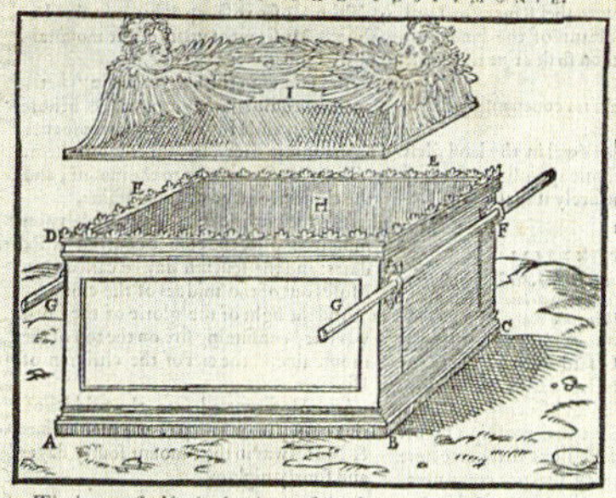

A B The length, two cubites and an halfe.
B C The breadth a cubite and an halfe.
A D The height a cubite and an halfe.
E E The golde crowne about the Arke.
F The foure rings of golde in the foure corners.
G The barres couered wt golde to put through the rings to cary the Arke.
H The inner parte of the Arke where the Testimonie was put.
I The Mercie seate, wc was the couering of the Arke: where were the two Cherubims, & whence ŷ oracle came.

15 The barres shal be in the rings of the Ar-
ke: they shal not be taken away from it.
16 So thou shalt put in the Arke the [f] Te-
stimonie which I shal giue thee.
17 Also thou shalt make a [*] [g] Merciseat of
pure golde, two cubites and an halfe lõg,
and a cubite and an halfe broad.
18 And thou shalt make two Cherubims of
golde: of worke beaten out with the ham-
mer shalt thou make them at ŷ two endes
of the Merciseat.
19 And the one Cherúb shalt thou make at
the one end, & the other Cherúb at ŷ o-
ther end: of *the matter* of the Merciseat shal
ye make the Cherubims, on the two endes
thereof.
20 And the Cherubims shal stretch their
wings on hie, couering the Merciseat with
their wings, & their faces one to an other:
to the Merciseat ward shal the faces of ŷ
Cherubims be.
21 And thou shalt put the Merciseat aboue
vpon the Arke, and in the Arke thou shalt
put ŷ Testimonie, which I wil giue thee,
22 And there I wil [*] declare my selfe vnto
thee, and from aboue the Merciseat * be-
twene the two Cherubims, which are vpõ
the Arke of the Testimonie, I wil tel thee
all things which I wil giue thee in cõman-
dement vnto the children of Israél.

f The stone tables, the rod of Aarõn and Manna, which were a testimonie of Gods presẽce.
* Or, couering, or, propiciatorie.
g There God appeared mercifully vnto them: and this was a figure of Christ.
* Or, meet with thee.
Nom. 7.89.

THE TABLE OF THE SHEWE BREAD.

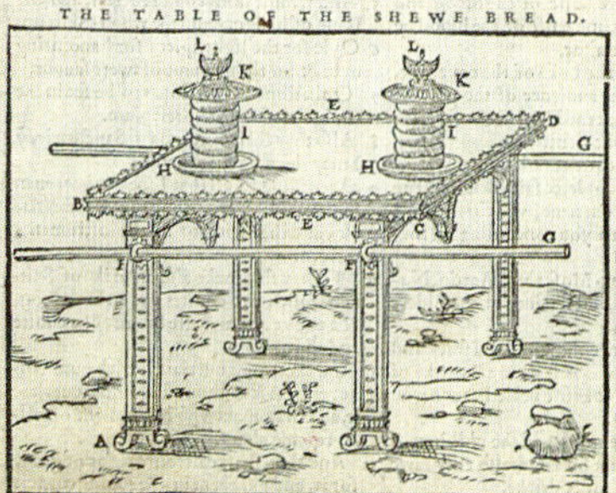

A B The height a cubite and an halfe.
B C The length two cubites.
C D The breadth a cubite.
E A crowne of golde aboue & beneth separated the one frõ the other by a border of an hand breadth thicke, wc declareth that the table was an hand breadth thicke.
F The foure rings.
G The barres to cary the table, which were put through ŷ rings.
H Dishes wherein ŷ shewe bread was put.
I The twelue cakes or loaues called the shewe bread.
K The goblets or couerings.
L The incense cuppes.

Chap. 37, 10.
23 ¶ * Thou shalt also make a table of Shit-
tim wood, of two cubites long, & one cu-
bite broad, and a cubite and an half hie:
24 And thou shalt couer it wt pure golde,
and make thereto a crowne of golde ro-
unde about.
25 Thou shalt also make vnto it a border
of [*] foure fingers rounde about: and thou
shalt make a golden crowne rounde about
the border thereof.
26 After, thou shalt make for it foure rings
of golde, & shalt put the rings in ŷ foure
corners that are in the foure fete thereof:
27 Ouer against the border shal the rings
be for places for barres, to beare the Ta-
ble.
28 And thou shalt make the barres of Shit-
tim wood, and shalt ouerlay them with
golde, that ŷ Table may be borne with
them.
29 Thou shalt make also [h] dishes for it, and
incens cups for it and couerings for it, and
goblets, wherewith it shalbe couered, *eue*
of fine golde shalt thou make them.
30 And thou shalt set vpõ the Table shew-
bread before me continually.

* Or, an hand bread.
h To set the bread vpon.

THE CANDELSTICKE.

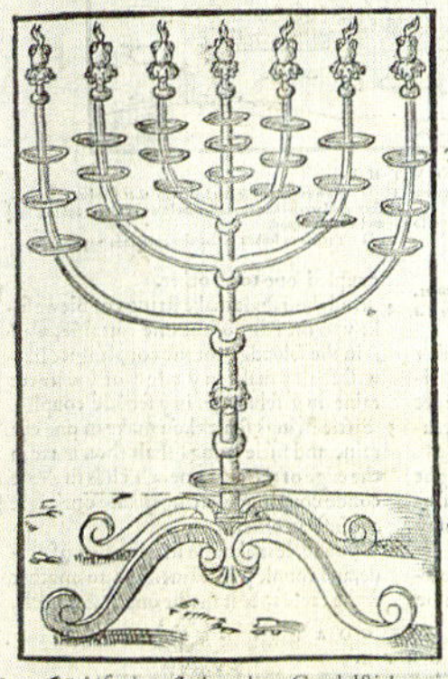

Because the facion of the candelstick is so plaine & euidẽt, it nedeth not to describe the particular partes thereof according to the ordre of lettres. Onely where as it is said in the 34 verse, that there shalbe foure bowles or cuppes in the cãdelsticke it must be understãd of the shaft or shãke: for there are but thre for euerie one of the other branches. Also the knoppes of the cãdelstick are those which are under the brãches as thei issue out of the shaft on ether side.

Chap. 37, 17.
31 ¶ * Also thou shalt make a Candelsticke
of pure golde: of [i] worke beaten out wt the
hãmer shal the Cãdelsticke be made, his
shaft, & his brãches, his bolles, his knops:
and his floures shal be of the same.
32 Six branches also shal come out of the
sides of it: thre branches of the Candel-
sticke out of the one side of it, and thre
branches of the Candelsticke out of the o-
ther side of it.
33 Thre bolles like vnto almondes, one
knop and *one* floure in one branche: and
thre bolles like almondes in the *other* brã-
che, one knop and *one* floure: so through
out the six branches that come out of the
Candelsticke.
34 And in the *shaft* of ŷ Candelsticke *shalbe*
foure bolles like vnto almõdes, his knops
& his floures.
35 And *there shalbe* a knop vnder two bran-
ches *made* thereof: & a knop vnder two brã
ches *made* thereof: and a knop vnder two
brãches *made* thereof according to the six
branches comming out of the Candel-
sticke.
36 Their knops and their branches shalbe
thereof. all this shalbe one beatẽ worke of
pure golde.
37 And ŷ shalt make the seuen lãpes the-
reof, & ŷ lãpes thereof shalt ŷ put theron,
to giue light toward that that is before it.
38 Also the snoffers & snoffedishes thereof
shal be of pure golde.
39 Of [k] a talẽt of fine golde shalt thou make
it with all these instruments.
40 * Loke therefore that thou make *them*
after their facion, that was shewed thee
in the mountaine.

i It shal not be molton, but beaten out of the lumpe of golde with ŷ hammer.
k This was ŷ talent weight of the temple & waied 120 pounde.
Ebr. 8, 5.
Act. 7, 44.

l. iiii.

Vernaculars across Europe

Vernacular Epic

40 *La Chanson de Roland* (with Plato, *Timaeus*, in the Latin translation of Chalcidius).
England; second quarter (?) of the 12th century.
ii + 55 (Plato) + 76 (Roland) leaves; 175 x 120 mm.

The earliest surviving manuscript of the greatest of the Old French epic poems known as *Chansons de Geste* presents tantalizing problems concerning its origins. The original composition of the poem may belong to the late 11th century, the period of the First Crusade. It has usually been assumed that this Anglo-Norman French text was adapted from a version composed in France itself. But it is equally possible that it was composed in Norman England: there is considerable evidence that in the first half of the 12th century the story was already well known in educated Anglo-Norman circles. The provenance of this manuscript partly depends on its relationship to the Latin text - dating from approximately the same time, but much more expertly produced - with which it shares its present Digby binding. The two parts were already together before Digby's time in the catalogue of the collection of Thomas Allen in 1622. But the 14th-century ex-libris of Oseney abbey, stating that the book had been given to the abbey by Master Henry de Langley, who studied at Oxford in the 1240s, refers only to the *Timaeus*.

The story is of the betrayal and slaughter by the Saracens of the rear-guard of Charlemagne's army (at Roncevaux in the Pyrenees), the death and glory won there by the Christian heroes Roland and Oliver, and Charlemagne's revenge. The *Chanson* is written in ten-syllabled lines, grouped together in stanzas or *laisses* of irregular length. The final syllables of the lines in every *laisse* are not rhymed but assonanced together - that is, all have the same vowel sound, but no regard is paid to the following consonants. The repetitions at vital moments in the narrative, the mysterious refrain 'AOI' at the end of some *laisses*, and the scruffy appearance of the manuscript all act as reminders of the origins of vernacular literature in oral recitation: it is tempting to imagine this book in the pocket of a travelling *jongleur*. But the final sentence is enigmatic: 'Ci falt la geste que Turoldus declinet'. Was Turoldus author, copyist, or *jongleur*?

Provenance: Bequeathed by Thomas Allen (1540-1632) to Sir Kenelm Digby (1603-65); given by Digby to the Bodleian, 1634.

Literature: Quarto cat. IX, cols. 19-20; eds. A. de Laborde, C. Samaran, *La Chanson de Roland. Reproduction phototypique du manuscrit Digby 23 de la Bodleian Library d'Oxford* (Roxburghe Club 182: Paris, 1932); P & A i, no. 475; M.B. Parkes, 'The Date of the Oxford Manuscript of La Chanson de Roland: Bodleian Library MS Digby 23', *Medioevo Romanzo* 10 (1985), 161-75, reprinted in *idem, Scribes, Scripts and Readers. Studies in the Communication, Presentation and Dissemination of Medieval Texts* (London/Rio Grande, 1991), 71-89.

MS. Digby 23, part II (fol. 32r)

Sire Rollant e uos sire oliuer.
Pur deu uos pri ne uos cuntraliez.
Ja li corners ne nos aureit mester.
Mais ne pur quant si est il asez melz.
Venget li reis si nus purrat venger.
Ja cil despaigne nen deiuent turner liez.
Nostre franceis i descendrunt a pied.
Truuerunt nos e morz e detrenchez.
Leuerunt nos en bieres sur sumers.
Si nus plurrunt de doel e de pitet.
Enfuerunt en aitres de musters.
Nen mangerunt ne lu ne porc ne chen.
Respunt Rollant sire mult dites bien. AOI.
Rollant ad mis lolifan a sa buche.
Empeint le ben par grant uertut le sunet.
Halt sunt li pui e la uoiz est mult lunge.
Granz .xxx. liwes loirent il respundre.
Karles loit e ses cumpaignes tutes.
Co dit li reis bataille funt nostre hume.
E guenelun li respundit encuntre.
Saltre le desist ia semblast grant mencunge. AOI.
Li quens Rollant par peine e par ahans.
Par grant dulor sunet sun olifan.
Par mi la buche en salt fors li cler sancs.
De sun ceruel le temple en est rumpant.
Del corn quil tient loie en est mult grant.
Karles lentent ki est as porz passant.
Naimes li duc loid si lescultent li franc.

Vernaculars across Europe

Troubadours and Courtly Love

41 Provençal *Chansonnier*.
Northern Italy; late 13th century.
ii + 266 pages; 205 x 115 mm.

In the Middle Ages Occitania, which stretched across the south of France (and of which Provence itself formed only a part) had its own language and culture, independent of political boundaries. Its troubadour poet-musicians of the 12th and 13th centuries created a new vernacular poetic language, and sang of courtly love, a code which was to influence the whole of European literature. Most of the 164 songs (by some 40 different troubadours) in this anthology are love lyrics. In making his request for love, the poet adopts a submissive stance and places his lady in a position of dominance: the relationship is akin to that of the knight swearing service to his lord. But the lady, though not necessarily married, is usually unattainable by virtue of social rank or physical distance. The true subject of these lyrics - almost all by male authors - is the emotional struggle of the lover: man is exalted by his desire, and his lady forms a mirror for his ideal self. The relationship between such poems and actual courtly society is unclear. Certainly the poet's search is for financial as well as for amorous rewards: 'The lady is an object of prestige for both lord and poet: praise of her attractions enhances the prestige of her husband's court; her favour enhances the poet's status within it' (Paterson).

The songs in this *chansonnier* were copied by a single scribe, probably a Venetian with a good knowledge of Provençal. The penwork initial on the page reproduced marks the beginning of a song by Raimbaut de Vaqueiras, one of the few troubadours to be knighted (*c.*1194). Despite having gone on crusade, Raimbaut's poems show little interest in martial prowess. His description of his patron's court is a far cry from the world of the *Chanson de Roland* (no. 38): 'In your court reign all graces: the giving of gifts and the courting of ladies, fine clothes, elegant armour, trumpets, games, viols and song...'.

Provenance: perhaps identifiable in the inventory of Niccolò III d'Este, Marchese of Ferrara, 1436; Nicolas-Claude Fabri de Peiresc (1580-1637), French antiquarian; Henri Joseph Thomassin de Mazauges (1684-1743), Provençal scholar; various 18th and early 19th-century owners; bequeathed by Francis Douce (1757-1834).

Literature: SC 21843; ed. W.P. Shepard, *The Oxford Provençal Chansonnier* (Elliott Monographs in the Romance Languages and Literatures: Princeton, 1927); E.G.R. Waters, review of Shepard, *Modern Language Review* 23 (1928), 367-71; ed. M. Tyssens, *Lyrique romane médiévale: La tradition des chansonniers* (Bibliothèque de la Faculté de Philosophie et Lettres de l'Université de Liège 258: Liège, 1991); L.M. Paterson, *The World of the Troubadours. Medieval Occitan Society, c.1100-c.1300* (Cambridge, 1993).

 MS. Douce 269 (p. 126)

CXXVI.

Vostre bel acuillimen.
Non uedez qe sabez faire.
De plus nous aus preiar gaire.
Tant soi espauentaz.
Car es de tan ric plais.
Ma ouidi retrais.
Centrels corals amadors.
no· Nont paratges aricors.
Enseignamen 7 beautaz.
Franqesa 7 gen parlar.
Gens acoillir 7 ontar.
Cortes ab gaia senblansa.
Vos fan sob autres ontansa.
Per qe ioi 7 solaz reuiu.
Ab uos 7 nais.
Vers calqe part biais.
Et nol mo fai dir amors.
Mas uer 7 uostras lausors.

Rambaut de uaqeira. by

Sauis 7 fols humils 7 orgoillos.
Scubes 7 larcs 7 uolpiz 7 ardiz.
Soi qan sesthai 7 iausenz 7 marriz.
Et sai esser plasenz 7 enoios.
Et uils 7 cars 7 uillans 7 cortes.
Auols 7 pros 7 conosc mals 7 bes.
Et ai de toz bos aips coi 7 saber.
Et sen ren faill fazo per non poder.
En toz afars soi sauis 7 zignos.
Mas midonz am tant qem sos enfoliz.
Ceill soi humils ou pez me fai 7 diz.
Et nai ergoill car es tan bella 7 pros.
Et soi cubes cab son bel cors iaqes

Vernaculars across Europe

Illustrating Dante

42 Dante, *Divina Commedia.*
Italy; third quarter of the 14th century.
vi + 154 pages; 355 x 235 mm.

The *Divine Comedy* was almost immediately perceived as a vernacular text unlike any other, an allegorical work akin to the Bible in its need for verbal and visual glossing. The earliest illustrated manuscripts were produced in Florence within a decade or two of Dante's death in 1321. It was not an easy text to translate into images, but the problem was not so much the idea of representing mystical experiences and supernatural realms - both of which were regularly depicted in Christian art - as the need for invention without the aid of a pre-existing pictorial tradition. Nevertheless, an accepted canon of scenes and compositions had been fixed by about the middle of the century.

The page reproduced shows the illustration to *Purgatorio* 10, in which Dante and Vergil gaze at marble reliefs representing examples of humility from the New Testament, the Old Testament, and Roman history. The Annunciation is a traditional composition. The relief in the middle shows oxen pulling a cart containing the Ark of the Covenant, but there is no sign of the other half of the scene, David dancing before it: already the copying (or miscopying) of a model has taken over from invention based on the text. The third example shows the Emperor Trajan (on horseback) halted by a weeping widow seeking justice.

The illustrations in this manuscript form a continuous series of narrative miniatures running across the lower margin of every page. The setting remains constant in each realm: black rocks and flames for the *Inferno*, bare parchment for the *Purgatorio*, a starry sky of blue and gold in the *Paradiso*. This frieze-like form of narration, designed to convey the sense of a journey, was adopted early on in the illustrative tradition as an alternative to the conventional insertion of miniatures into the columns of the text. Although not entirely new, this technique remained a rarity in the history of European medieval book illumination.

Provenance: Thomas Coke, first Earl of Leicester, who probably bought it in Italy, 1714-17; Holkham Hall MS. 514; accepted by HM Treasury from the executors of the fifth Earl in part satisfaction of Capital Transfer Tax, and allocated to the Bodleian, 1981.

Literature: P. Brieger, M. Meiss, C.S. Singleton, *Illuminated Manuscripts of the Divine Comedy* (London, 1970); M. Rotili, *I codici danteschi miniati a Napoli* (Miniatura e Arti Minori in Campania 7: Naples, 1972), no. 1; M. Roddewig, *Dante Alighieri. Die göttliche Komödie. Vergleichende Bestandsaufnahme der Commedia-Handschriften* (Hiersemanns bibliographische Handbücher 4: Stuttgart, 1984), no. 364.

MS. Holkham misc. 48
(p. 75)

Vernaculars across Europe

Literature in Translation

43 *Le Roman de Troyle.*
Western France; *c.*1480.
i + 77 leaves; 280 x 205 mm.

The rise of vernacular literature may seem to have divided Europeans from each other: but in fact the same stories were translated and re-translated, so that in many ways a common literary culture was maintained despite linguistic differences. This is a French prose translation of Boccaccio's *Filostrato* of *c.*1335: the translator was probably Louis de Beauvau (*c.*1417-62), who served René d'Anjou in Naples in 1438-42, and was Seneschal of Anjou from 1445 to 1458. The illustration in two parts shows Troyle kissing Briseyda (as the heroine is called here), and the couple in bed. In Boccaccio's tale, Troilo tries to preserve his life against the dangers of war and the wounds of love. In telling the story of seduction and betrayal, the narrator, who identifies with the lovesick hero, attempts to persuade his own beloved to return, and at the same time relieves his suffering by an appeal to the compassion of an audience of courtly lovers.

The combination of the legend of Troy and the theme of courtly love ensured the success of Boccaccio's work. But whereas Louis de Beauvau's translation remained faithful to its source, Chaucer's *Troilus and Criseyde* (finished by 1388) is a reworking as much as a translation. How Chaucer acquired his copy of Boccaccio's text is unknown: very few libraries in northern Europe contained the works of Boccaccio before 1400, though this is not the only evidence for Chaucer's interest in contemporary Italian literature. In his hands the scope of the story is widened, and greater attention paid to the character of Criseyde and to a comparison of the virtues of religious and courtly love. This reworking of the model was sanctioned by contemporary literary theory: Petrarch likened literary imitation to the relationship between a father and his son, and, following Horace, he compared the creative process to the activity of bees making honey.

Provenance: Jean d'Albret d'Orval (*c.*1460-1524), or another member of his family; L.J.Gaignat sale, 1769, no. 2342; Francis Douce, 1791; bequeathed to the Bodleian, 1834.

Literature: SC 21905; P & A i, no. 729; M.G. Hanly, *Boccaccio, Beauvau, Chaucer: Troilus and Criseyde. Four Perspectives on Influence* (Norman, Oklahoma, 1990); A.C. de la Mare, C. Reynolds, 'Illustrated Boccacio Manuscripts in Oxford Libraries', *Studi sul Boccaccio* 20 (1991-2), 45-72, pp. 63-6.

 MS. Douce 331 (fol. 26r)

lauoit bien senti venir
Et affin quil le congneust
bien toussit vne fois ou
deux Et pour ce que lestre
ne luy ennuyast souuen
teffois parloit assez hault
et auancoit chin quil sen
alast dormir en disant quelle
auoit si grant sommeil
quelle ne se pouoit plus
soustenir Apres ce que
chin fut couche et lostel

fut demoure vuyde si tar
doit a briseyda de venir
ou lieu ou estoit troyle se
crettement mis Lequel
comme il la sentit venir
se dressa a elle et auecques
chere pieuse luy ala alen
contre tout quoyement et a loi
sir et lattendant prest et appareille
de luy obeyr come seruiteur
doit faire a sa dame mais
tresse et amie

La belle tenoit
vng flambeau
en la main et
toute seulle descendit les
degrez et vit troylle qui
lattendoit Lequel elle salua

A Vernacular Parody

44 Miguel de Cervantes Saauedra, *El ingenioso hidalgo Don Quixote de la Mancha*. Madrid: for Iuan de la Cuesta, 1605, 4°. 332 leaves; 185 x 125 mm.

The continued cultural cohesion of European literary traditions is demonstrated by the ease with which even vernacular texts could obtain an international distribution. The genre of knightly romances was popular in most European countries. This common literary tradition ensured that a spoof could gain an international audience. The English translation of Don Quixote, from 1612, was the first in a series of vernacular translations. Thomas Shelton, the translator, was probably a Roman Catholic Irishman who had fled the country in or shortly before 1604. Another sign of the instant popularity was the appearance of a sequel not written by Cervantes himself. Don Quixote was also soon abridged and appeared in cheap formats as a chapbook.

Despite tense relations between England and Spain, the London bookseller John Bill went to Spain on Sir Thomas Bodley's behalf in 1604, during a period in which tensions had lessened. He had planned to visit all the important book-producing centres there. However, he got no further than Seville, where he felt intimidated by the anti-English atmosphere and left the country. He had managed to buy a substantial number of Spanish books, among which was this copy of the first edition of *Don Quixote*. The cost of these purchases was covered by the Earl of Southampton, Henry Wriothesley, Shakespeare's patron, a book collector himself who perhaps had a special Spanish interest because of his involvement in the Earl of Essex's sack of Cadiz in 1597. The early presence of Don Quixote in the Bodleian is a surprise: Sir Thomas aimed at forming an academic library and had explicitly expressed his desire to keep out vernacular works, which were mostly fiction and therefore not relevant to the studies conducted at Oxford.

Provenance: acquired by Sir Thomas Bodley's agent in Spain in 1604.

Literature: *A Catalogue of Hispanic Manuscripts and Books before 1700 from the Bodleian Library and Oxford College Libraries Exhibited at the Taylor Institution* (Oxford, 1962), no. 156.

 4° C 31 Art. (the title-page)

EL INGENIOSO HIDALGO DON QVIXOTE DE LA MANCHA,

Compuesto por Miguel de Ceruantes Saauedra.

DIRIGIDO AL DVQVE DE BEIAR, Marques de Gibraleon, Conde de Benalcaçar, y Bañares, Vizconde de la Puebla de Alcozer, Señor de las villas de Capilla, Curiel, y Burguillos.

Año, 1605.

CON PRIVILEGIO,

EN MADRID, Por Iuan de la Cuesta.

Vendese en casa de Francisco de Robles, librero del Rey nro señor.

Music

45 Secular and religious music.
Northern Italy; second quarter of the 15th century.
v + 141 paper leaves; 295 x 215 mm.

This compilation contains songs in French, Italian, and Latin; but for these, unlike the other vernacular songs exhibited (nos 38, 39), the music is included. Musical experimentation can be seen as the development of a European technical language: this manuscript was written by an Italian scribe (probably in the Veneto), but most of the composers represented are from northern Europe. The size and quality of the compilation make it one of the most important sources for early 15th-century polyphonic music. Some 325 pieces are included, the majority annotated with the names of their composers, some of whom are not recorded anywhere else. The manuscript is overwhelmingly the most important source for the songs of Guillaume Dufay: the page reproduced begins with his 'Ce moys de May'. The publication of the manuscript in 1899 by Sir John Stainer, the Heather Professor of Music at Oxford, under the title *Dufay and his Contemporaries*, was a landmark in the rediscovery of medieval polyphonic song. A complete facsimile edition, edited by Dr. David Fallows, is shortly to be published by the University of Chicago Press.

Provenance: Matteo Luigi Canonici (1727-c.1806); bought by the Bodleian as part of the Canonici collection, 1817.

Literature: Quarto cat. III, col. 583; H. Schoop, *Entstehung und Verwendung der Handschrift Oxford Bodleian Library, Canonici misc. 213* (Publikationen der schweizerischen musikforschenden Gesellschaft, Series 2, vol. 24: Berne, 1971); G.M. Boone, *Dufay's Early Chansons: Chronology and Style in the Manuscript Oxford, Bodleian Library, Canonici misc. 213* (unpublished Ph.D. dissertation: Harvard University, 1987).

MS. Canon. Misc. 213
(fol. 17v)

Guillermus du Fay.
Tenor.
Contratenor.
Petrus. Fontaine.

Vernaculars across Europe

The Language of Architecture

46 Vitruvius, *Architecture ou Art de bien bastire.*
Paris: for J. Gazeau, B. Hérissault Barbé and heirs of J. Barbé, 1547, 2°.
184 leaves; 380 x 250 mm.

The classical treatise on architecture, written before 27 BC by Vitruvius, was also translated into vernaculars, helping to create a common European idiom of architecture, literally as well as metaphorically. The translation of a technical text like Vitruvius into the vernacular was dependent on a knowledge of the language of builders and craftsmen, not always familiar to the educated men who spent their time studying classical texts. Vitruvius's text is not always very clear, and the classical norms which could often be learned from it could be considerably clarified by illustration, although some illustrations created more problems than they solved. This French translation, by Jean Martin, contains illustrations by Jean Goujon, in part derived from three different editions from Italy. Vitruvius had dedicated his work to the Emperor Augustus, his employer, a fact which the translator puts to good use in his dedication of this edition to Henri II, King of France, whose buildings at the Louvre were much inspired by Vitruvian ideals. Much of the decoration of the Louvre was made by Goujon, including the caryatids in the Salle des Caryatides, one of the most splendid results of Henri's building activity at the Louvre. We here show the first plate in the volume, displaying Goujon's illustration to Vitruvius's discussion of the caryatids.

Our copy of the book belonged to Diane de Poitiers, Henri II's mistress, and is still in the binding made for her. It is of white kid skin tooled in silver, now oxidized, and with an interlace pattern from which the original, probably black, enamel has now been worn away. The oblong brass frame is intended to hold a piece of parchment with the title of the book written on it. The binding is decorated with Diane's and Henri's entwined initials and with the crescent, and bow and arrows of the goddess Diana.

Provenance: Diane de Poitiers; bequeathed to the Bodleian by Francis Douce (1757-1834).

Literature: H. Nixon, *Sixteenth-century Gilt-Tooled Bookbindings in the Pierpont Morgan Library* (New York, 1971), 142-43; R. Mortimer, *Harvard College Library, Department of Printing and Graphic Arts Catalogue of Books and Manuscripts. Part I: French 16th Century Books* (Cambridge, Mass., 1964), no. 549.

Douce V subt. 1 (fol. 6v [marked 2 verso])

Colonnes Caryatides.

Neighbours

In the Middle Ages distant countries were conceived in fantastic terms: the Marvels of the East describes the monstrous beings found amongst the peoples of Asia (no. 47). The genre of travellers' tales mixed fact and fiction: our famous manuscript of the travels of Marco Polo is bound together with accounts of the wonders experienced in the East by Alexander the Great (no. 48). Too close to be inhabited by monsters, Russia was viewed even in the 16th century as a distant, wild, and mysterious country (no. 53).

At the same time, commercial and cultural contacts with Europe's closest neighbours were frequent, and Arabic scholars were of the greatest importance for medieval European students of philosophy, science, and medicine (no. 49). Europe's attempts to understand its Islamic neighbours were mostly based on a desire to convert them: the 12th-century translation of the Koran into Latin was intended to enable Christians to understand, and therefore to counter, the challenge of Islam (no. 50). In the 16th century Roman Catholic doctrine was translated into Arabic to provide material for Christian missionaries (no. 52). Often European self-definition was based on the definition of someone or something else as alien. The unity of Christendom was part of the ideology - if not always the political reality - behind the Crusades against the Islamic possessors of the Holy Land (no. 51). After conquering the last Muslim-held territories on the Iberian peninsula, the Christian kingdom of Spain could reassert its European identity by expelling the resident non-Christian populations, both Jews and Muslims (no. 32).

Spain went on to take the lead in the European conquest of Central and South America. Increased technical competence lay behind both exploration and conquest: both cartography and navigation depended on advances in astronomy (no. 54). Astrology and astronomy were expensive disciplines which were largely dependent on royal patronage (nos 55 and 56). Hevelius's maps of the moon illustrate the extension of European mapmaking to our nearest neighbour in the universe (no. 57).

Neighbours

Marvels of the East

47 *Marvels of the East* (with astronomical material, and a calendar).
England; *c.*1120-40.
i + 53 leaves; 145 x 100 mm.

Medieval Europeans knew more about the stars than about Asia. This pocket-sized manuscript contains information about both subjects. The astronomical part was derived from classical sources passed down through Carolingian copies: it contains texts and pictures concerning the sun and moon, the constellations and signs of the zodiac, the atmosphere, winds, rainbows, and shooting stars.

The text of the Marvels of the East claimed both classical and eye-witness authority. Probably composed in the 4th century AD, it purported to be a letter written by one Pharasmanes to the Emperor Hadrian, describing what he had seen on a journey to the East. The account of the monstrous races and animals had its origin in ancient Greek descriptions of the fabulous peoples of India. The Marvels enjoyed the same kind of popularity in the Middle Ages as the Alexander legends (see no. 53), with the development of which it was closely linked. The earliest illustrated manuscripts of the *Marvels* are Anglo-Saxon, and both text and picture cycle here are closely related to the version in London, British Library, Cotton MS. Tiberius B. V (produced in the mid-11th century, perhaps at Christ Church Canterbury), which has an Old English translation alongside the Latin text.

The page reproduced here shows an example of the 'Lertices', a small beast with the ears of a donkey, the fleece of a sheep, and the feet of a bird; and one of a race of men eight feet tall and eight feet broad, who, lacking heads, have eyes and mouth in the middle of their chests. From this tradition, such creatures entered the repertoire of European Romanesque art, appearing either independently with other grotesque creations or, as on the tympanum at Vézelay, being used to portray the pagan peoples destined to be converted to Christianity by the mission of the Apostles.

Provenance: Ralph Hopwoode (16th century); acquired by the Bodleian between 1605 and 1611.

Literature: SC 2144; ed. M.R. James, *Marvels of the East. A Full Reproduction of the Three Known Copies* (Roxburghe Club 177: Oxford, 1929); P & A iii, no. 156; J.B. Friedman, *The Monstrous Races in Medieval Art and Thought* (Cambridge, Mass., 1981).

 MS. Bodl. 614 (fol. 41r)

25
141

Sunt & alie bestiole in brixonte que lertices
appellantur. auribus asininis. uellere ouino.
pedibus auium.

Est & alia in
sula in bri
xonte ad meri
die in q̄ nascunt̄
hoīes sine capi
tibus. qui in
pectore habent
oculos & os alti
sunt pedū octo.
& lati similit̄
pedum octo.

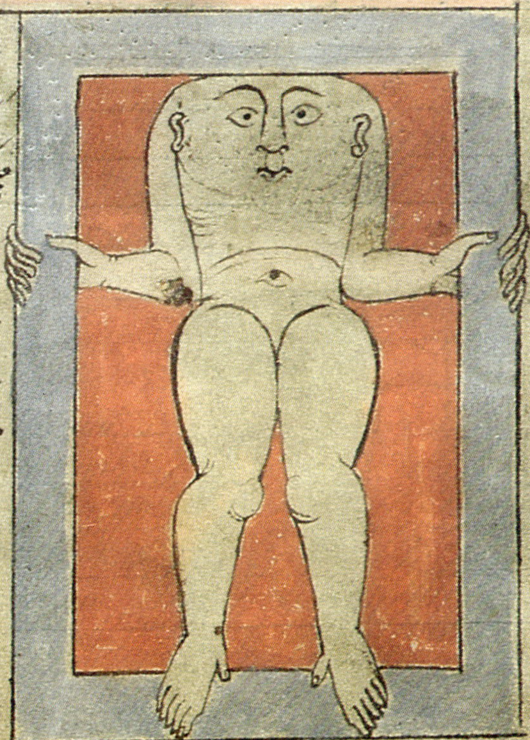

Neighbours

Travels

48 Marco Polo, *Li Livres du Graunt Caam* (with Alexander Romances).
England; early 15th century.
x + 274 leaves; 420 x 295 mm.

Marco Polo travelled overland with his father and uncle to China, where he worked in the service of Kublai Khan for twenty years before returning to Venice. Captured by the Genoese in 1298, he dictated the account of his travels whilst in prison. Translated into many languages, it provided one of the eariest detailed descriptions of the Far East. In this case the text was illustrated with thirty-eight miniatures, beginning with the famous scene of the embarkation at Venice. The party is depicted at more than one moment, following the conventions of medieval pictorial narrative; but at the same time the miniature looks forward to the development of the new genres of landscape and town-scape painting. Some of the city's landmarks, such as the horses of St. Mark's, are clearly represented. The artist, who was probably the leader of a team of illuminators, signed himself 'Iohannes' in another miniature; his workshop may have been in London, another great sea-port.

Although Marco Polo's was an eye-witness account, this copy was bound together with two Alexander romances - accounts of the wonders of the East encountered by Alexander in India, built up with many accretions, and almost entirely fictional - to form a book of travellers' tales not as different in spirit from no. 47 as might at first sight appear. The first of the Alexander romances in the manuscript is in French verse: its illumination, finished (possibly in Tournai) in 1344, consists of miniatures and a famous series of marginal scenes. The second, contemporary with the Marco Polo and also illustrated, recounts the story of Alexander's communications with the Brahmans of India, and is a unique Middle English version in a West Midlands dialect.

Provenance: Richard Woodville, first Earl Rivers (bought in London, 1466); various 16th-century owners; acquired by the Bodleian in *c.*1603-4 from an unrecorded source.

Literature: SC 2464; ed. M.R. James, *The Romance of Alexander. A Collotype Facsimile of MS. Bodley 264* (Oxford, 1933) (not including the Marco Polo section); P & A i, no. 297, and iii, nos 792-3; ed. R. Latham, *The Travels of Marco Polo* (Folio Society: London, 1968), reproducing many of the miniatures from this manuscript; A.G. Watson, *Catalogue of Dated and Datable Manuscripts c.435-1600 in Oxford Libraries* (2 vols: Oxford, 1984), no. 74.

 MS. Bodl. 264 (fol. 218r)

Neighbours

Arabic Medicine

49 Albucasis, *Chirurgia* (with other medical texts).
Southern France or Italy; first half of the 13th century.
i + 179 leaves; 330 x 225 mm.

In early medieval Europe, surgery was essentially limited to cautery and bloodletting. Classical knowledge of anatomy and surgical techniques was reintroduced into Europe by the translation of Arabic texts into Latin. The Islamic Empire had taken over centres of Greek philosophy and science in Egypt, Mesopotamia, and Syria; the caliphs of 9th-century Baghdad patronized the translation of Greek and Syriac texts into Arabic. Thus it was Muslim scholars who had the opportunity to assimilate and develop the Greek inheritance in philosophy, mathematics, medicine, and astronomy.

The transmission of the medical sources into Europe began with the work of Constantinus Africanus (died *c.*1087), a north African Arab who converted to Christianity and became a monk at Monte Cassino. In the wake of Christian military successes in Spain, southern Italy, and Sicily (especially the reconquest of Toledo in 1085), the process accelerated, with large numbers of translations produced in the 12th century by European scholars such as Gerard of Cremona and Adelard of Bath, as well as by the Muslims and Jews with whom they mixed in a cosmopolitan culture. The production of translations was accompanied by the revival of dissections and operations in the medical schools at Salerno, Bologna, and Montpellier — and in due course by the regulation by European rulers of medical practice and the training of physicians.

Albucasis was a physician in Cordoba in the second half of the 10th century. His monumental medical compendium was divided into thirty books, some of which circulated separately. The last book, on surgery, was translated by Gerard of Cremona and became the main surgical handbook in Europe. The translations initially imitated the organization and layout of the Arabic version: the drawings of surgical instruments are an integral part, illustrating the description in the text of the instruments' manufacture and appearance. Illustrations of the instruments' use did not become popular until the 14th and 15th centuries.

Provenance: given to the Bodleian by John Pooley between 1606 and 1611.

Literature: SC 2461; P & A ii, no. 74; E. Irblich, 'Einfluß von Vorlage und Text im Hinblick auf kodikologische Erscheinungsformen am Beispiel der Überlieferung der *Chirurgia* des Abu'l Qāsim Ḫalaf Ibn 'Abbās al-Zahrāuī vom 13. Jahrhundert bis 1500', in *Paläographie 1981. Colloquium des Comité International de Paléographie: München, 15.-18. September 1981*, ed. G. Silagi (Münchner Beiträge zur Mediävistik und Renaissance-Forschung 32: Munich, 1982), 209-31.

 MS. Bodl. 360 (fol. 21v)

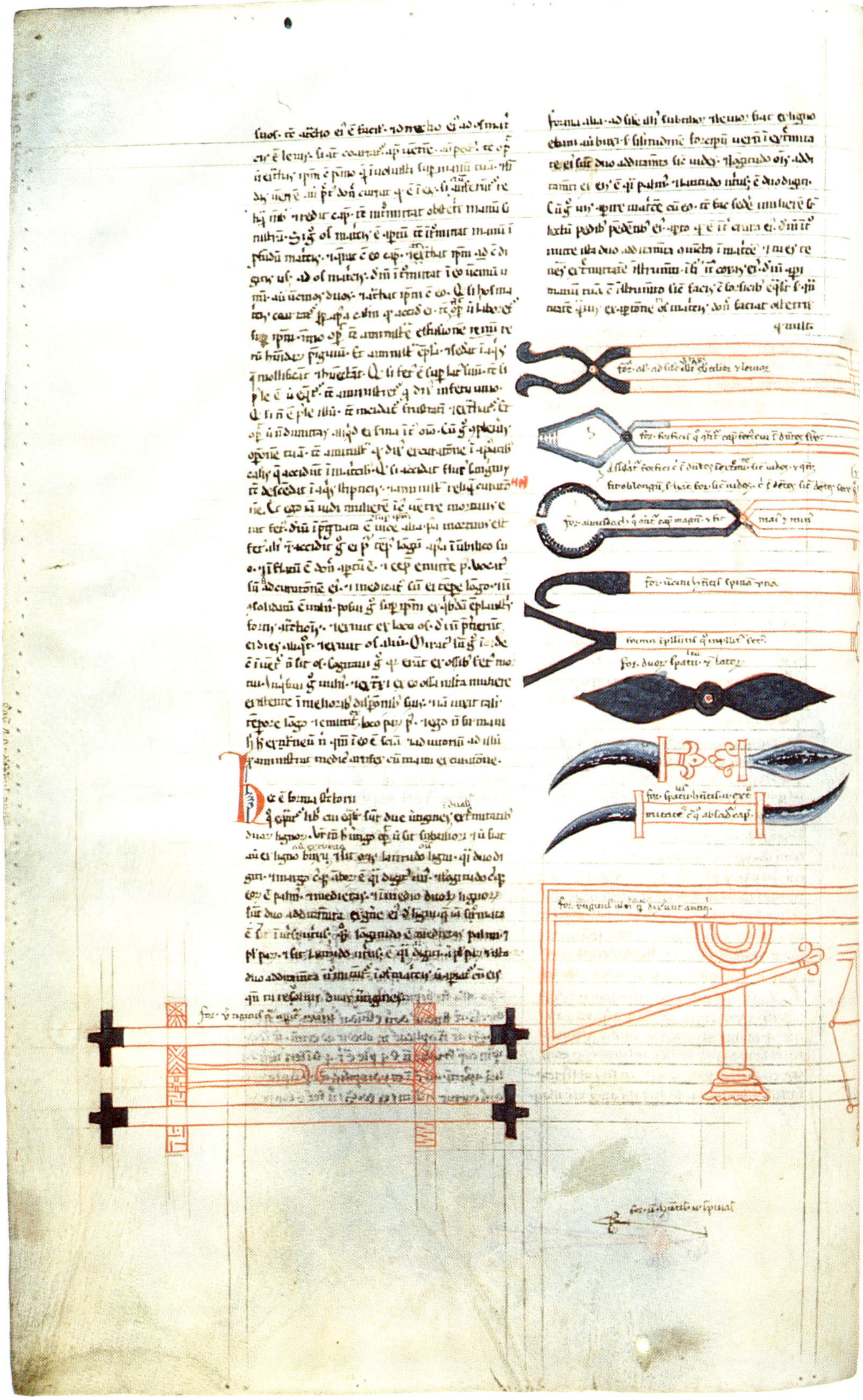

Neighbours

Translating Islam

50 Latin translation of the Koran (with other translations).
England; late 13th century.
207 leaves; 225 x 140 mm.

For medieval European Christians, the existence of Islam posed a problem. What was it, and why did it exist? Should one find out more, or stay apart to avoid contamination? The choice was between crusade, commerce, co-existence, and conversion (Southern). Western writers before the 12th century knew almost nothing of Islam as a religion: there was too much fear to permit the indulgence of detached inquiry.

Travelling in Spain in 1141-2 on a visitation of Benedictine monasteries, Peter the Venerable, abbot of Cluny, met the English astronomer and geometrician Robert of Ketton, and his friend Herman of Dalmatia. Both were accomplished Arabists. Peter commissioned them to prepare several translations, including Robert of Ketton's of the Koran, and Herman's of the treatises *De generatione Mahumet* and *Doctrina Mahumet*. These, together with Peter of Toledo's translation of the Apology falsely attributed to the 9th-century Arab Christian al-Kindi, and Peter's own *Liber contra sectam sive haeresim Saracenorum*, are known as the Toledan-Cluniac collection, part of which is found in this manuscript.

The purpose of the first complete translation of the Koran into any language was to facilitate the refutation of Islamic doctrine. Peter believed that ignorance of the tenets of Islam on the part of Christians would lead to a lack of resistance to it. He invited St. Bernard to use the sources thus gathered; but Bernard, perceiving the danger as military rather than theological, was preoccupied with the Second Crusade. So Peter, believing that the approach should be made not 'as our people often do, by arms, but by words', wrote the refutation himself.

Though the work commissioned by Peter had no dramatic effect, the European outlook was in certain respects to change during the following century, with the demise of the Crusader Kingdom (though not of the crusading ideal (no. 51)), the appearance of the Mongols (putting Islam itself under pressure), the experience of travellers, traders, and missionaries, and the assimilation of Arabic learning through translations (no. 49).

Provenance: Bury St. Edmunds abbey, 14th century; John Selden (1584-1654); Selden's collection acquired by the Bodleian, partly by bequest, partly from his executors.

Literature: SC 3419; M.-T. d'Alverny, 'Deux traductions latines du Coran au Moyen Age', *Archives d'histoire doctrinale et littéraire du Moyen Age* 16 (1947-8), 69-131; R.W. Southern, *Western Views of Islam in the Middle Ages* (Cambridge, Mass., 1962); J. Kritzeck, *Peter the Venerable and Islam* (Princeton Oriental Studies 23: Princeton, 1964).

MS. Selden Supra 31 (fol. 33r)

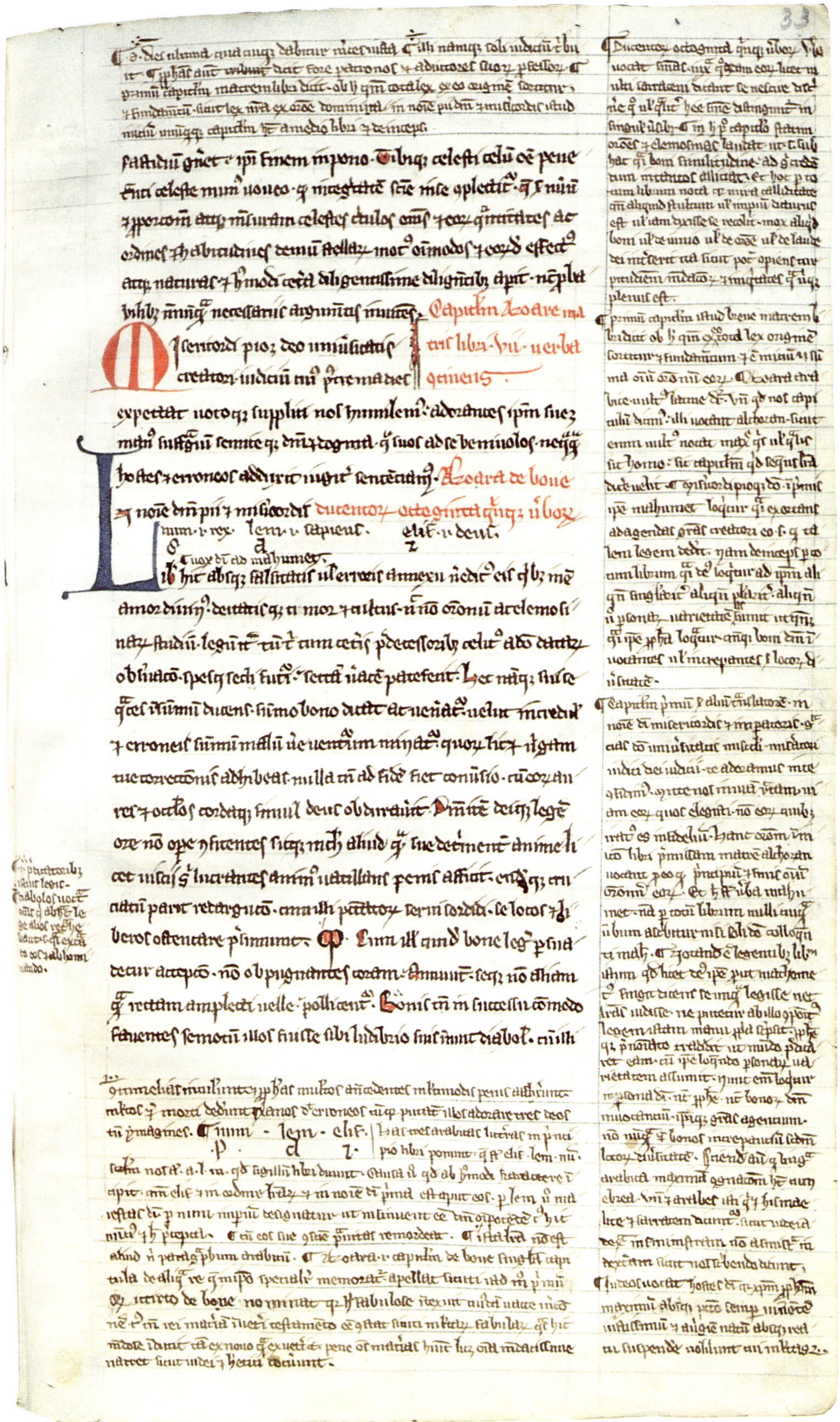

Neighbours

Crusading

51 Marino Sanudo, *Secreta Fidelium Crucis.*
Venice; before 1321.
ii + 211 leaves; 285 x 220 mm.

The Frankish Kingdom of Jerusalem finally ended with the fall of Acre, its last stronghold, in 1291. Yet at the courts of the Pope and the King of France, new plans were discussed for the recovery of the Holy Land. Marino Sanudo (1270-1343), a Venetian merchant, had visited Acre when it was still in Christian hands. His plan for the recapture of 'Outremer' was outlined in his book, 'Secrets of the Faithful of the Cross'. The power of Mamluk Egypt was to be undermined by a combination of economic embargo, political alliances, and military pressure. When the trade embargo had had its desired effect, Egypt could be conquered by a small sea-borne expeditionary force, which would be followed by a mass crusade. The concentration on trade was to be expected from someone of Sanudo's background: in Venice the idea of a crusade was more a matter of public policy than of chivalric adventure.

Sanudo devoted the rest of his life to persuading European leaders of the virtues of his plan, especially at Paris and in the papal court at Avignon. In this campaign it was vital that those in the corridors of power should be able to consult copies of Sanudo's book; to this end he commissioned numerous copies in Venice at his own expense. This copy belongs to the 'First Redaction', but contains additions in various hands of items which were subsequently incorporated into the Second, including an account of the examination of the plan by a papal commission in 1321. Maps of the world, the Middle East, Jerusalem, and Acre are appended for reference, and miniatures are enticingly placed towards the beginning of the book. The manuscript was given to Robert, count of Boulogne, a powerful influence in French politics, who took the cross in 1313 and led an embassy to Pope John XXII to discuss the crusade in 1323. Sanudo died a disappointed man, leaving instructions in his will that his book should always be available for consultation. The crusading ideal was kept alive in poetry, romances, and chronicles: it was to retain a tenacious hold over the minds of western Europeans.

Provenance: Robert VII, comte de Boulogne et d'Auvergne; King Charles V of France (1338-80); bequeathed to the Bodleian by Thomas Tanner (1674-1735).

Literature: P & A ii, no. 118; B. Degenhart, A. Schmitt, 'Marino Sanudo und Paolino Veneto. Zwei Literaten des 14. Jahrhunderts in ihrer Wirkung auf Buchillustrierung und Kartographie in Venedig, Avignon und Neapel', *Römisches Jahrbuch für Kunst-geschichte* 14 (1973), 1-137; C.J. Tyerman, 'Marino Sanudo Torsello and the Lost Crusade: Lobbying in the Fourteenth Century', *Transactions of the Royal Historical Society* 32 (1982), 57-73.

 MS. Tanner 190 (fol. 22r)

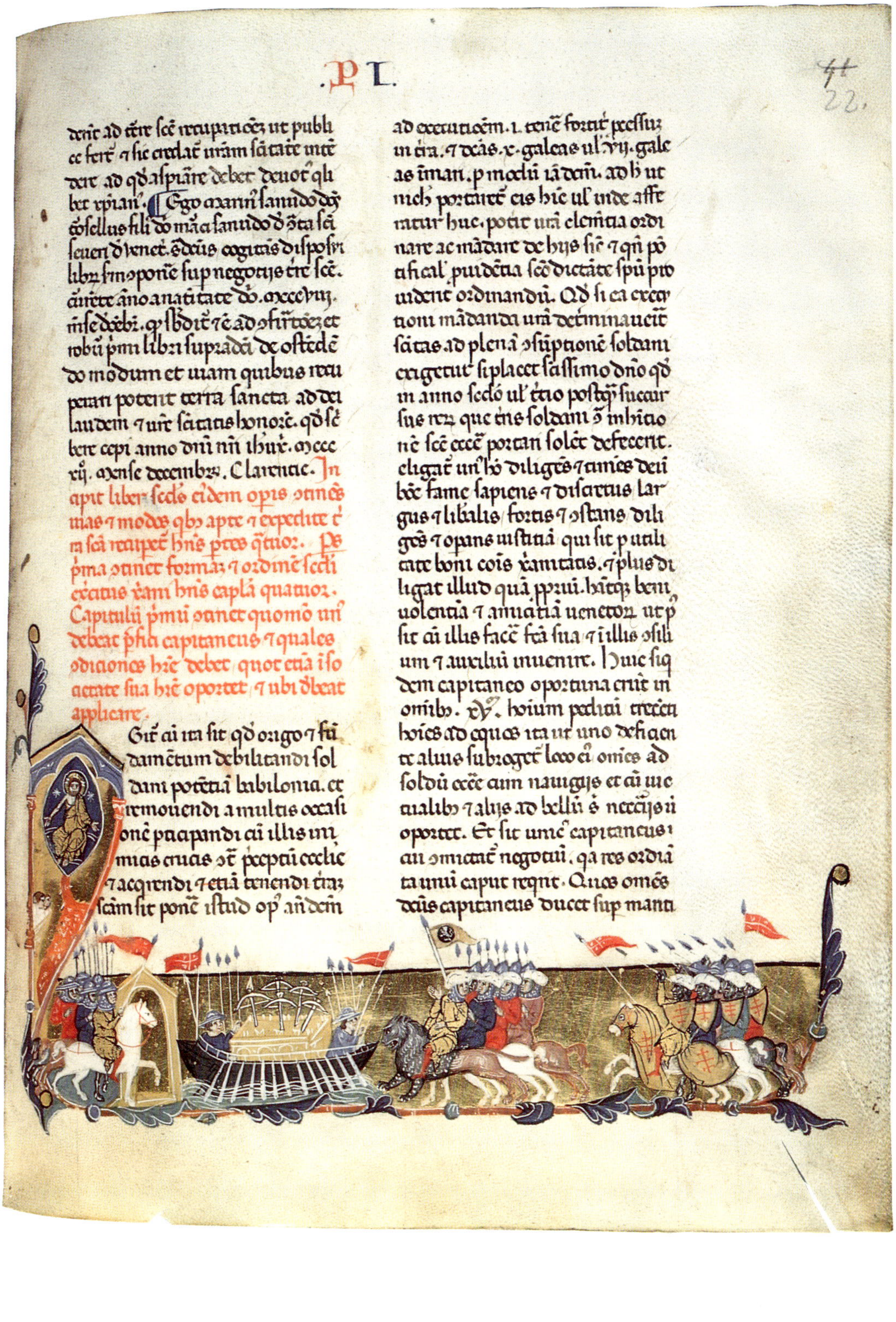

Neighbours

Translating Christianity

52 *Brevis Orthodoxæ fidei professio quæ ex præscripto Sanctæ Sedis Apostolicæ ab Orientalibus ad Sacrosanctæ Romanæ Ecclesiæ unitatem venientibus facienda proponitur* [in Latin and Arabic].
Rome: in typographia Medicea, 1595, 4°. 16 leaves; 220 x 140 mm.

The age of crusades was over, but confrontation with Europe's Islamic neighbours continued. Since they had first gained a foothold on European territory in 1345 the Turks of the expanding Ottoman Empire had replaced the Arabs as the main threat to Christendom. The final fall of the Roman Empire of the East in 1453, was followed by further conquest culminating at the siege of Vienna in 1529 and the humiliation of the Holy Roman Emperor Charles V who was compelled to pay annual tribute to the Sultan. While Europe expanded overseas, its very centre was under serious threat.

While armed conflict continued, attempts to convert Europe's Islamic neighbours continued. The Papal presses in Rome produced much material for this purpose in a variety of languages, and employing a wide variety of fonts. The desire to convert encouraged familiarity with non-European languages, alphabets and scripts. Perhaps least exotic among these, was the Arabic language, which was probably also aimed at converting the Turks, who used Arabic for religious purposes. This little work was aimed at converting Europe's nearest neighbours towards the south-east, not to Christianity merely, but to counter-reformation Roman orthodoxy of the era after the Council of Trent.

Our copy, however, never served its purpose, for it is contained in a fine binding made for the Roman family of Torres, possibly for Ludovico de Torres, before he was made a cardinal (1606). With a group of other bindings on books emanating from the Vatican Press in these years, it has been attributed to a Roman workshop working for members of the papal court.

Provenance: John Selden (1584-1654); presented with his other printed books to the Bodleian in 1659 by the executors of John Selden's will.

Literature: *Fine Bindings 1500-1700 from Oxford Libraries* (Bodleian Library, Oxford, 1968), no. 21.

4° P 19 Th. Seld.
(fols. 13v and 14r)

Cum ergo prandiſſent, dixit Simoni Petro Ieſus; Simon Iona, diligis me plus his? dicit ei etiam Domine, tu ſcis quia amo te. Dicit ei Ieſus: Paſce mihi agnos meos. Dicit ei iterum. Simon Iona diligis me? ait illi etiam Domine, tu ſcis, quia amo te. Dicit ei; Paſce mihi agnos meos. Dicit ei tertio: Simon Iona amas me? contriſtatus eſt Petrus, quia dixit ei tertio amas me, & dicit ei; Domine tu omnia noſti, tu ſcis quia amo te. Dicit ei; Paſce mihi oues meas. Ioan. vlt.

ولما تناولوا الغدا قال يسوع لسمعان الصفآء. ياسمعان ابن يونا تحبني اكثر من هولاء ✿ قال له نعم ياسيدي انت تعلم اني احبك. قال له يسوع ارع لي خرافي. ثم قال له مرة ثانية ياسمعان ابن يونا تحبني. قال له نعم ياسيدي انت تعلم اني احبك. قال له ارع لي كباشي.

ثم عاوده القول له دفعةً ثالثه ياسمعان ابن يونا تحبني وصعب علي الصفاء اذ قال له ثلث مرات تحبني. فقال ياسيدي انت تعلم بكل شي وانت تعلم اني احبك قال له ارع لي نعاجي ✿

Neighbours

The Borders of Europe

53 Sigismund von Herberstein, *Rerum Moscoviticarum commentarii.* [Vienna:] J. Singriener (1549), 2°. 84 leaves; 285 x 250 mm.

The Grand Duchy of Muscovy aroused tremendous curiosity in the 16th century, as commerce brought it into ever closer contact with the rest of Europe. The West looked upon the Russians with ethnographic interest, as a group which was not quite part of the same world as their own, despite the similarities of religion and of language, already noted by Conrad Gesner. These illustrations show how a westerner saw the costumes of the Russians. In this exhibition, commercial interest in Russia is also demonstrated by the willingness of the Muscovy Company in London to pay for the translation of Cortés's book on navigation (no. 54).

Knowledge about foreign countries could be obtained through ambassadors, who would often acquire books on their travels (see no. 3). They would also be likely to write about their travels. Herberstein, who spoke Russian, went to Russia twice as ambassador for Charles V, the Holy Roman Emperor, in 1517 and 1526. In his book he described Russia as a barbarous tyranny, using literary motifs which recall Greek and Roman descriptions of the reigns of the Oriental despots. The line between Europeans and barbarians was clearly drawn in Herberstein's mind. The illustrations also display an ethnographic interest in the manners of foreign peoples. Herberstein's work was, for a long time, a standard source for western Europeans writing about Russia.

Provenance: 'Collegii Societatis Jesu 1605'; 19th-century stamp of the Königliche und Kaiserliche Bibliothek, Klagenfurt; acquired by the Bodleian between 1862 and *c.*1883.

Literature: C. Haraner, 'Die zeitgenössischen lateinischen Drucke der Moscovia Herbersteins und ihre Entstehungsgeschichte. Ein Beitrag zur Editionstechnik im 16.Jahrhundert', *Humanistica Lovaniensia* 31 (1982), 141-63; ed. G. Pfersky, *Sigismund von Herberstein, Kaiserliche Gesandter und Begründer der Ruslandskunde und die Europäische Diplomatie* (Graz, 1989).

 3 Δ 252 (fols. 16v-17r)

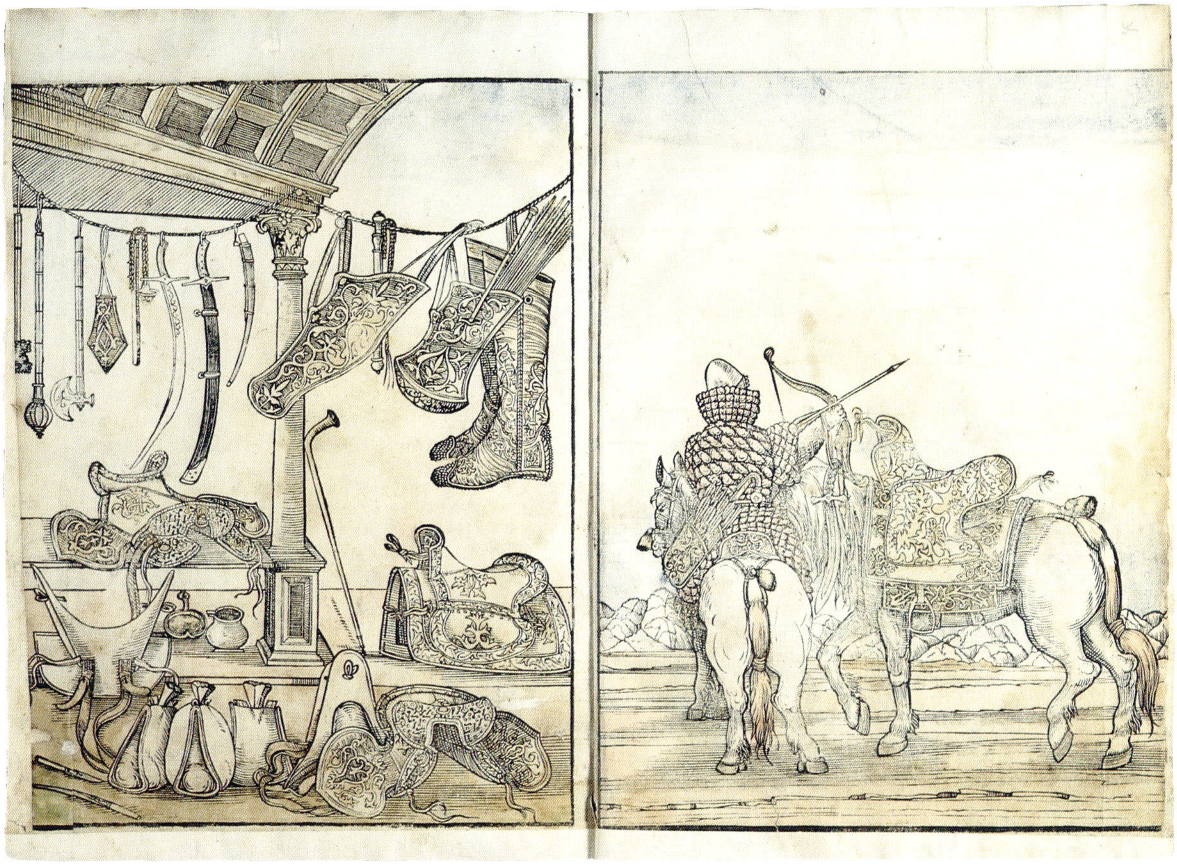

Neighbours

Exploration and Expansion

54 Martín Cortés, *Breve compendio de la sphera y de la arte de nauigar.* Seville: A. Alvares, 1556, 2°. 95 leaves; 270 x 195 mm.

The commercial explorations of the East, the discovery of America, and the consequent encounter with completely different cultures reinforced the consciousness of Europe as a unit. For this expansion, navigation was a necessity. The manual of navigation by Cortés (1532-89) was first published in 1551. The remaining sheets of the 1551 edition were reissued in 1556, with only the last two leaves reset. Our copy is of this second issue.

The work was soon translated into several languages. During the reign of Mary Tudor and Philip of Spain, Stephen Borough (1525-84) visited Spain and brought the book back with him. He had persuaded the Muscovy Company to pay for an English translation by Richard Eden (1521[?]-76) who had been employed in the English treasury of Philip. Published in 1561, a late result of the close relations between Spain and England, this translation became a standard work on navigation for English explorers and pirates of the 16th century.

Cortés dedicated the original work to Charles V, Roman Emperor and King of Spain. The opening displayed here shows Cortés pointing towards foreign shores, and commanding the universe, aided by navigational tools. In the letter of dedication Cortés addressed Charles as the creator of a new Golden Age, a new Saturnian reign, recalling the themes of Vergil's praise of Augustus (see also no. 9). Cortés struck a high tone invoking the religious and moral renewal of Charles's reign, which went hand in hand with the restoration of learning, both practical and theoretical. Navigation was one of the practical arts which had prospered during Charles's wise reign. Cortés recalled navigation as an ancient art, referring to the voyage of the Argo — quietly forgetting that, in ancient literature, navigation was an element of the myth of the fall of man from a state of innocence: it brought trade, greed and corruption, and ended the Golden Age.

Provenance: in the Bodleian by 1605.

 H 4.20(3) Art. (fol. 1v)

MANꝰ NRE
SE ET DNS
CIT HECOIA
EXCEL
FE

Neighbours

Astrology

55 Petrus Apianus, *Astronomicum Caesareum.*
Ingolstadt [P. Apianus], 1540, 2°. 82 leaves; 465 x 315 mm.

Apianus (1495-1552) was the imperial astronomer and his *Astronomicum* is probably the most spectacular book printed in the 16th century. The work was printed in Ingolstadt by Apianus at his own cost and dedicated to Charles V, the Holy Roman Emperor, and his brother Ferdinand, the future Emperor. This was a book meant for the rich and powerful, not for scholars, and provides another example of the way in which books were used as gifts for diplomatic purposes (see no. 3). Nicholas Wotton reported in 1544 from the Diet of Speyer that Apianus would give Henry VIII a copy of the *Astronomicum Caesareum*: he would otherwise not be able to get hold of it, as it was printed in only sixteen or seventeen copies. This was an exaggeration — some thirty-five copies are known — but it was a rare book: Edmund Halley (1656-1742) tried in vain to get hold of it, because it contained Apianus's observations of the appearance in 1531 of the comet which now bears Halley's name. It is not by chance that the book was produced in southern Germany. A tradition of high-quality instrument making made it possible to find craftsmen who understood what was to be illustrated and who had the skills to prepare plates for such a book. While the production was a technical feat, this book was not Apianus's most distinguished contribution to science. Giving the spurious impression of providing the precision of scientific instruments, the revolving plates reproduce information which could just as easily be represented in tables. But the talented or wealthy amateur, who might wish to understand his horoscope, would find the volvelles convenient ready reckoners. The chief aim was to satisfy the astrological interests of his powerful patrons: all examples for the use of the volvelles relate to dates of astrological importance for Charles V and Ferdinand. The volvelle shown here on the left, enables you to establish lunar and solar eclipses. By aligning the various rotating parts according to information provided in tables, you can make the volvelle reproduce the lunar and solar position of a specific date. The heads and the tails of the dragon represent the nodes of the constellation *drago*, the points at which the sun and the moon are in conjunction. An eclipse can be predicted for the time when one of the nodes of the dragon lines up with the image of a darkened moon or sun on the rotating part which represents the conjunction of the earth with the sun.

Provenance: 'Du Burseun' [17th century?]; probably acquired in 1842.

Literature: S. A. Ionides, 'Caesar's Astronomy', *Osiris* 1 (1936), 356-389; P. Apian, *Astronomicum caesareum.* Facsimile und Textband von D. Wattenberg (Leipzig, 1987); *State Papers. Volume IX. King Henry VIII*, part V,4 (London, 1849), 701-03.

 Arch. B b.7 (fols. 27v-28r)

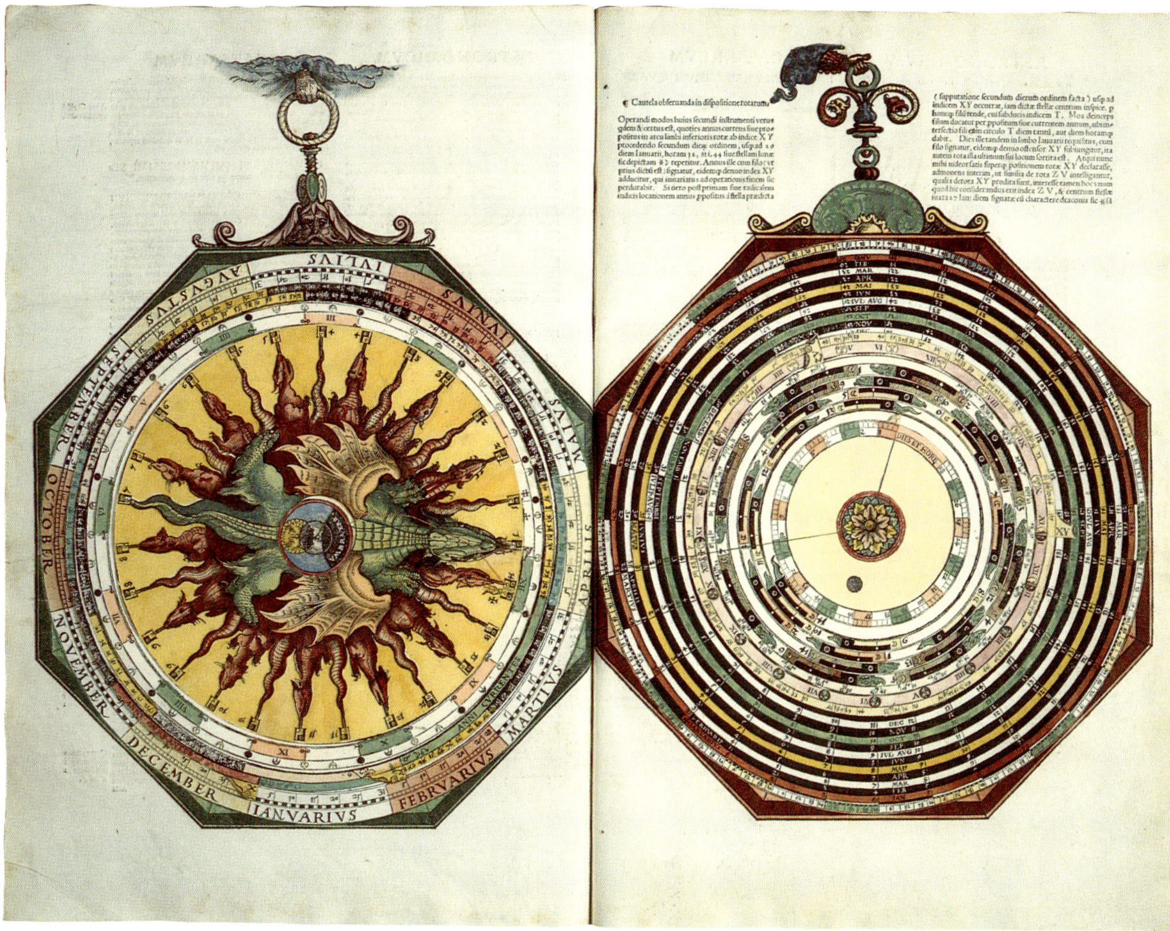
Cautela obseruanda in dispositione rotarum
IVLIVS
AVGVSTVS
SEPTEMBER
OCTOBER
NOVEMBER
DECEMBER
IANVARIVS
FEBRVARIVS
MARTIVS
APRILIS
MAIVS

Neighbours

Instruments of Observation

56 Tycho Brahe, *Astronomiae instauratae mechanica.*
Wandsbeck [Philip von Ohr for] Tycho Brahe, 1598, 2°. 42 + 36 leaves; 340 x 250 mm.

The expansion of European knowledge of the world continued into space. More than any earlier astronomer, Tycho Brahe (1546-1601) registered his results systematically, using instruments built to unprecedented specifications. When his royal sponsor complained that his instrument making was too slow, Brahe answered: 'If they were made well enough, they were made fast enough'. We show the great mural quadrant, its scale cast in brass. Also on the wall is a painting made by the Augsburg artist Thobias Gemperlinus. The radius of the quadrant was so long — *c.*1.97 metres — that each minute of every degree on the scale could be subdivided, allowing readings accurate to within five or ten seconds. Previously, readings with a variation of ten minutes were considered accurate enough. The quadrant was aligned towards celestial south. As a planet passed the meridian it was observed through one of the two movable sights on the quadrant. Combined with a cylinder fixed in the opening in the wall, these formed parallel sights. Brahe thus avoided the inaccuracy inherent in circular sights, where it had to be estimated when an object occurred centrally. He read on the scale the position of the planet in relation to his meridian and horizon. By timing intervals between planets as they passed his meridian, he could establish their relative positions. Highly accurate for the 16th century, Brahe's clocks — depicted in front of the observer — could be used for measuring short timespans. For longer periods, clocks could not be used for astronomical purposes — indeed astronomical time was used for correcting even the most accurate of clocks.

A wealthy nobleman, he had been favoured by Frederik II, King of Denmark, but, in 1597, Brahe fell out of favour with his successor Christian IV and left Denmark. He found a new sponsor in the Holy Roman Emperor, Rudolph II, and on his way to Prague he produced this book, using the printing presses from his observatory. Containing a manuscript appendix with Brahe's stellar observations, our handcoloured copy was presented to Grimani, the Doge of Venice, on 15 February 1599. Brahe had heard of a planned Venetian astronomical expedition to Alexandria, and hoped he could persuade the Doge that some observations might be made for him.

Provenance: given to Doge Grimani by Brahe; acquired by Henry Wotton (1568-1639) who donated it to the Bodleian in 1633; Wotton assumed that it was given by Brahe to the Biblioteca Marciana which, however, still possesses its own presentation copy.

Literature: V. Noren, 'New Light on Tycho's Instruments', *Journal for the History of Astronomy* 4 (1973), 25-45; J. Field, 'What Is Scientific about Scientific Instruments?', *Nuncius* 3,2 (1988), 1-26; Brahe's poem to Grimani reproduced in D. Rogers, *The Bodleian Library and its Treasures 1320-1700* (Henley, 1991), 74-75.

 Arch. B c.3 (fol. 11v)

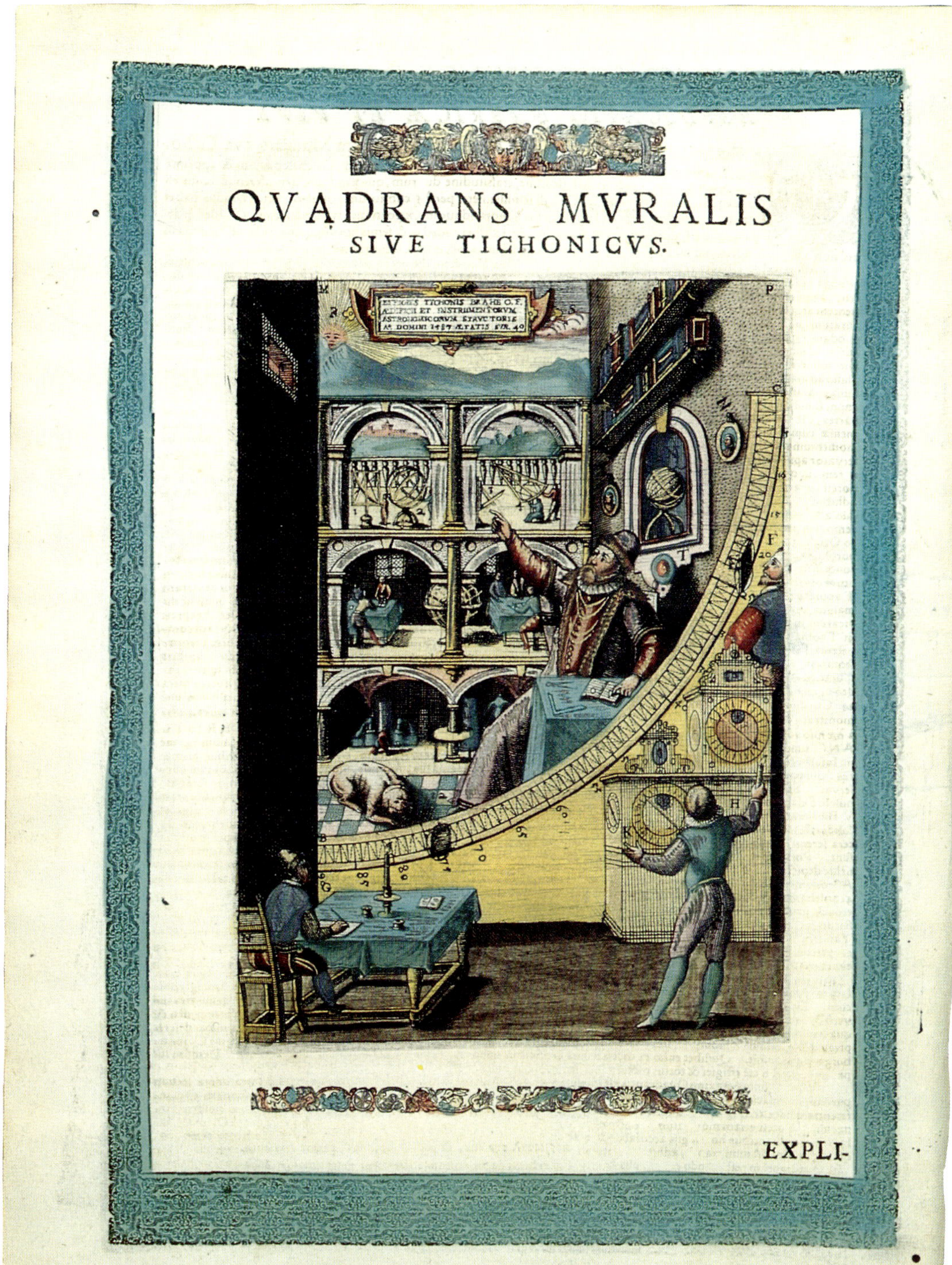
QVADRANS MVRALIS
SIVE TICHONICVS.
EXPLI-

Neighbours

Mapping the Moon

57 Johannes Hevelius, *Selenographia sive Lunae descriptio*. Gdańsk: Hünefeld for the author, 1647, 2°. 563 pp. and 89 plates; 350 x 220 mm.

Like Brahe (no. 56), Hevelius (1611-1687) was a wealthy man: it required funds to be an astronomer. He was born into a wealthy German-speaking family of brewers in Danzig, now Gdańsk in Poland. While Germany was ruined by the Thirty Years' War, the Gdańsk brewery financed Hevelius's instruments and publications. He presented copies to the Bodleian of almost all his works. This copy contains his manuscript dedication to the Bodleian and is contained in a lavish binding, made by Hünefeld, the Gdańsk printer. A similar but more elaborate binding also made by Hünefeld is found on the copy of the *Selenographia* dedicated to Louis XIV, now in the Bibliothèque Nationale in Paris. The copy in Paris is hand-coloured in silver and gold. Hevelius must have perceived the gift to Louis XIV as a gift of a luxury item, whereas the Bodleian was seen as a working institution which was to make his works available to the scholarly world. An effusive letter of thanks from the University of Oxford was sent to Hevelius on 19 November 1650. He was in close correspondence with scientists all over Europe, particularly in England, a fact recognized in his election to the Royal Society in 1664.

Hevelius named his observatories *Stellaeburgum* and *Uraniburgum* after Brahe's two Danish observatories, and saw himself as Brahe's successor. Hevelius's most famous observatory was a large platform built over several roof-tops in Gdańsk. The measurements for the *Selenographia* were made in his first observatory, however, where most of the instruments were similar to and based on those used by Tycho. His telescopes, however, were not. They were the basis for the observation of the moon, which profoundly changed our knowledge of our closest neighbour in the universe. Previous illustrations of the moon had been illustrative material, subsidiary to written descriptions. Hevelius built his own instruments, made his own observations, drawings and engravings; no intermediary distorted his observations. Based not on art, but on observation, the plates were intended themselves to communicate astronomical information.

Provenance: presented to the Bodleian by the author.

Literature: W. Winkler, A. van Helden, 'Johannes Hevelius and the Visual Language of Astronomy', in *Renaissance and Revolution. Humanists, Scholars, Craftsmen and Natural Philosophers in Early Modern Europe*, eds. J. Field and F. James (Cambridge, 1994), 97-116; D. Rogers, *The Bodleian Library and its Treasures 1320-1700* (Henley, 1991): binding on p. 110, inscription on p. 112, a map on p. 113; *Excerpta ex litteris... ad J. Hevelium ... studio J. E. Olhoffii* (Gdańsk, 1583), 26-28.

fol. BS 62 (plate 39, facing page 364)

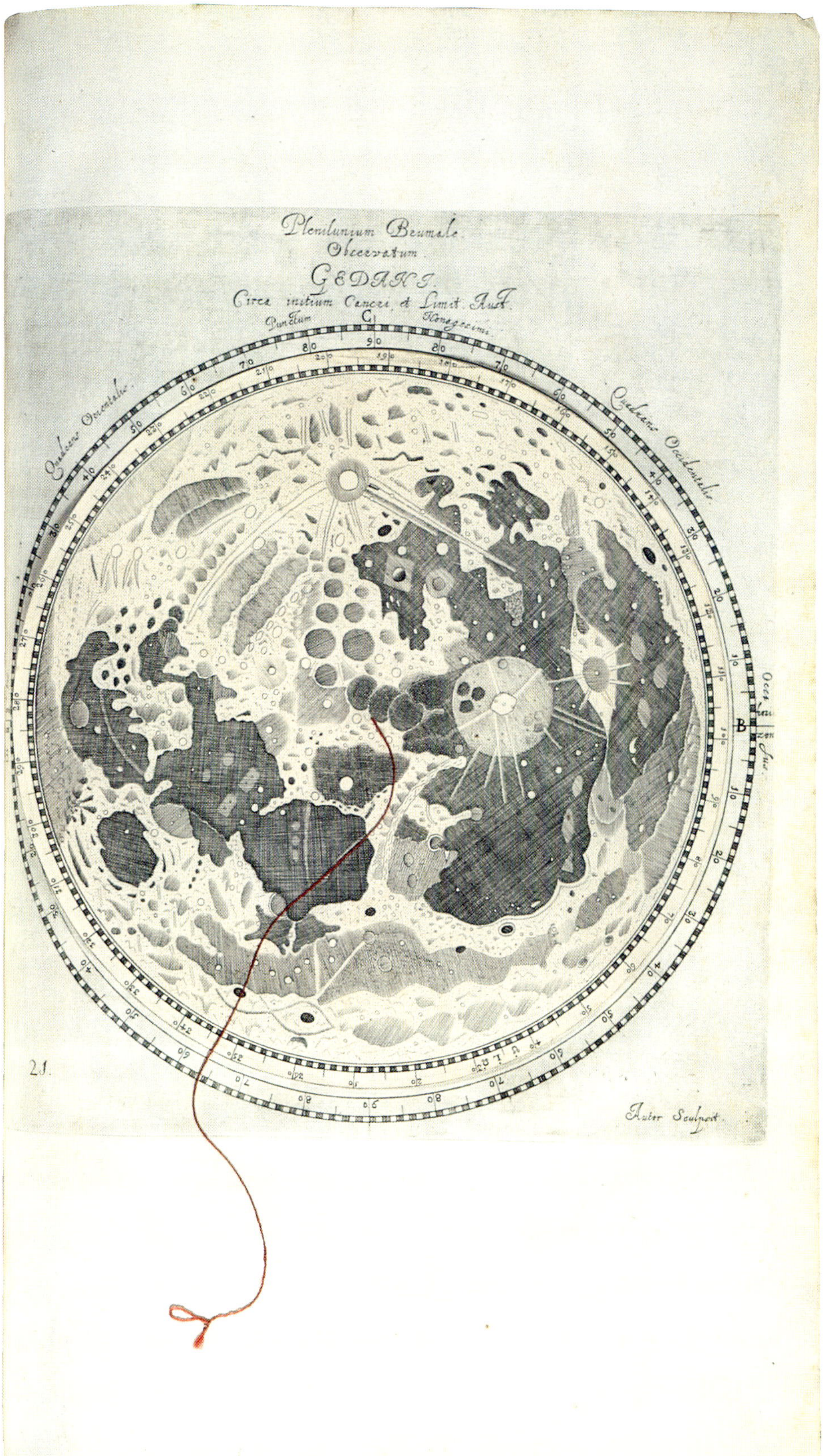
Plenilunium Brumale
Observatum
GEDANI
Circa initium Cancri, et Limit. Aust.
Punctum
C
Horizontalis
B
21.
Autor Sculpsit.

Conspectus of Shelfmarks

Manuscripts

MS. Auct. F. 2. 13	no. 10
MS. Bodl. 130	no. 24
MS. Bodl. 264	no. 48
MS. Bodl. 360	no. 49
MS. Bodl. 565	no. 5
MS. Bodl. 614	no. 47
MS. Bodl. 959	no. 38
MS. Broxbourne 83.1	no. 15
MS. Canon. Gr. 122	no. 37
MS. Canon. Misc. 213	no. 45
MS. Canon. Misc. 378	no. 8
MS. D'Orville 77 MS.	no. 1
D'Orville 78 MS.	no. 11
D'Orville 301	no. 28
MS. Digby 23	no. 40
MS. Douce 269	no. 41
MS. Douce 331	no. 43
MS. Douce 389	no. 6
MS. Douce 390	no. 2
MS. Hatton 48	no. 17
MS. Holkham misc. 47	no. 22
MS. Holkham misc. 48	no. 42
MS. Junius 25	no. 35
MS. Laud Gr. 35	no. 14
MS. Rawl. B. 514	no. 34
MS. Selden Supra 31	no. 50
MS. Tanner 190	no. 51

Printed books

165444 a.29	no. 27
Arch. B b.7	no. 55
Arch. B b.10	no. 16
Arch. B b.12	no. 4
Arch. B c.3	no. 56
H 4.20(3) Art.	no. 54
4° C 31 Art.	no. 44
Auct. 1Q 1.7	no. 19
Auct. 7Q 2.19	no. 18
Auct. 1R 2.2	no. 29
Auct. 1R 3.17	no. 30
Auct. L 1.1	no. 13
Auct. L 1.9	no. 12
Auct. M 3.15	no. 36
Bib. Eng. 1560 d.1	no. 39
Broxb. 95.4	no. 23
Broxb. 95.24(1)	no. 7
Byw. A 3.16(2)	no. 31
Byw. B 3.5	no. 33
3 Δ 252	no. 53
Douce 305	no. 3
Douce D subt. 41(2)	no. 21
Douce FF 59	no. 20
Douce G subt. 54	no. 25
Douce G subt. 7	no. 9
Douce V subt. 1	no. 46
fol. BS 62	no. 57
Opp. fol. 724	no. 32
RR. W.168	no. 26
4° P 19 Th. Seld.	no. 52